# GradeAid with Practice Tests

*for*

Lefton and Brannon

# Psychology

## Eighth Edition

*prepared by*

## Andrew H. Ryan, Jr.
University of South Carolina

Boston   New York   San Francisco
Mexico City   Montreal   Toronto   London   Madrid   Munich   Paris
Hong Kong   Singapore   Tokyo   Cape Town   Sydney

ISBN  0-205-37990-7

Printed in the United States of America

10  9  8  7  6  5  4  3  2          08  07  06  05  04  03  02

*To Nana*

# Contents

# Preface

*Grade Aid Study Guide* has been written with one goal in mind: to help students learn more from *Psychology, Eighth Edition*. Proven learning strategies are incorporated throughout the study guide in an easy-to-use format that will encourage students to become active participants in the learning process. The focus will be on learning, not on memorizing. Each chapter will begin by establishing learning objectives. The most efficient learning process involves distributed practice and the learning objective used properly provide these logical breaks. Mastering the learning objectives will increase confidence. Being relaxed and confident are keys to successful learning and examination preparation.

This *Grade Aid* study guide prepares the student by providing various exercises designed to maximize learning. The study guide contains dozens of learning exercises tied to the learning objectives in the text. In addition to teaching students to learn, *Grade Aid* challenges students to become *critical thinkers* by encouraging them to evaluate the research and generate personal meaning for the concepts presented in *Psychology*.

*Grade Aid* uses several techniques to optimize student learning:

1. Establishes clear learning objectives logically linked to the student text.

2. Provides various methods of learning in addition to the active reading material, including self-paced exercises, and comprehensicve *Self-Tests* that prepare the student for course exams.

3. Encourages students to establish schedules and goals for studying, to take breaks from studying, and to reward themselves for progress.

4. Encourages critical thinking about facts, issues, and methodologies.

5. Provides Term Identification Glossaries to clarify difficult words.

# HOW TO STUDY AND HOW TO LEARN

What does it take to learn and remember?

Educational (or instructional) psychologists focus their attention on instruction and academic learning and know a lot about what it takes for a person to learn in school. The information in this section comes primarily from their research findings about teaching, thinking, and learning.

The three most important characteristics of effective study are:

➢ Being actively involved in the learning process.

➢ Making new information meaningful by linking your existing life experiences and knowledge (what you already know) to new information (what you are learning for the first time).

➢ Taking responsibility for your own learning.

These characteristics are important to learning for several reasons. The first characteristic, *active learning* or *active participation*, means that you interact with new information so that it becomes alive and challenging. Instead of passively yawning over lifeless facts that refuse to stay in mind long enough even to pass a test, an active learner makes the facts alive and important by wrestling and dancing with them and really getting to know them. By simply using your own thoughts, asking and answering your own questions, and organizing information in ways that make sense to you, you become an active learner. When you are an active learner, the facts become more than facts—they become meaningful and stay with you. This suggests the second characteristic of effective learning.

To *generate personal meaning* out of new material (so that it becomes relevant to your life and needs), you must find ways to connect yourself, your knowledge, and your life experiences to the material you are studying. People have a natural tendency to do this, but by knowing that learning and memory are enhanced when you create personal meaning, you will be more likely in the future to do it intentionally. When you can relate new information to your own life by connecting it to your past or present, to problems you need to solve, or to events in the world, you make it important, and you are much more likely to understand it, remember it, and use it.

The third characteristic of effective study, *taking responsibility for your own learning*, is essential, because no one can do your learning for you. We do not learn much just by being present in class and skimming over printed words on a page. To learn means to change, and to change we must experience things for ourselves. Teachers (and textbooks) can present ideas and try to make them interesting; but only you can learn those ideas for yourself, and only you can make them meaningful to your life. For this reason, it is important to take responsibility not only for how you go about learning, but also for how you will shape and mold the ideas that are presented to you.

## DEVELOPING GOOD STUDY SKILLS

Remember trying to use a computer for the first time? You knew it could perform wonders, but you did not understand the new language required to operate it, or you tried the mouse and felt like you were suddenly totally uncoordinated. The first time you made a mistake or got a strange error message on the screen, you probably didn't feel so bad, but by the second or third time, you began to feel like maybe you were not cut out probably didn't feel so bad, but by the second or third time, you began to feel like maybe you were not cut out for computers. If you had friends who were catching on more easily, you probably began to feel still more frustrated (see *Chapter 14* in the Lefton and Brannon text for undersatnding stress and frustration).

The point is this: lacking the appropriate skills makes any task harder than it should be. In *Chapter 11* of your textbook, you will learn the key factors in motivation. You will learn that when people do not have the necessary skills or do not know what is expected of them, they experience failure, become frustrated, and lose their motivation to try. A lack of motivation is neither innate nor necessarily a fault in the individual; it may just mean that someone never learned the skills or values necessary to make the job worthwhile. When you have the necessary skills, your task, even though it may be difficult, will become easier and more rewarding. It may even be fun. This lesson is designed to teach efficient and effective study skills which, assuming that you use them, will help you with this and other courses as well.

## Review Your Educational and Professional Goals

Each time you begin a new class, you will find it useful to think about why you are taking the class and decide how it fits in with your long-term educational and professional goals. For example, you are currently enrolled in introductory psychology. Will this class help you with your professional goals? With your personal life? Is it a class required for your major? If so, why? Decide what value this class has for you and try to keep it in mind throughout the term.

Knowing how the class is meaningful to you will help motivate you to study and master the material presented. If you cannot think of a personally or educationally meaningful reason for taking the class, perhaps you should talk to your teacher or a school counselor. Almost every class has value, but pinpointing the value may be difficult. In any case, a lack of interest in the class from the outset will probably lead you to struggle through, feel frustrated, and continually wish the semester would end. This attitude is not conducive to good study skills.

## Scheduling Study Time

Once you have attended the first session of each of your classes, plan a study schedule based on the workload you expect to have for each class, your personal needs, your family's needs, and any other obligations you may have. Frequently people are not realistic about their time and think they can do more in a given period than they actually can. When planning your class and study schedule try hard to be reasonable: allow time for the unexpected, and remember you have obligations other than school. If you do not plan for these things and for "play/relax" time, you will end up having to take time for them anyway, and be forced to break or readjust your educational commitments. Remember, your study schedule is just as important as your class schedule. If you commit yourself to a realistic study schedule, you should be able to fulfill all your obligations, including school, much more smoothly.

If you work full or part-time, it is important to plan your class schedule so that you are enrolled in a few classes each semester that have little or no homework along with one or two classes that do. A student who works full-time should seriously consider being a part-time student since it is almost impossible to study four or five subjects well without a full-time commitment.

Some of my most successful students in my more than 20 years of teaching psychology have been the busiest students in class: students with jobs or family obligations and students carrying an extremely heavy courseload. What separated these students from the rest was their ability to organize. To be a well-organized student you begin each term by making a calendar of the due dates for every course. You should include all tests, papers, projects, personal dates to remember and most importantly, personal time. Personal time is time you set aside for yourself to relax and reward yourself for your hard work. This time does not have to be alone, just personal.

When planning your class and study schedule, try to mix your subjects. Also, when constructing your study sessions, plan to study several subjects at a time, each for about one hour, rather than one subject for several hours. Research indicates this is a much more efficient study tactic.

You will find it easier to fulfill your study schedule if you have a specific place to study. Select a quiet, well-illuminated place and always sit at a desk or table. If you study at home, be sure to move away from the television and family activities.

## How to Deal with a Short Attention Span

The average college student can read for only twelve minutes before drifting away from a book and falling into a daydream. Since daydreaming interferes with learning, knowing how to control it helps. You will find that using the *As you read...* section of the study guide will, to some extent, automatically decrease the number of daydreams you have while reading *Psychology*. In addition, if you set small goals, take breaks from your study sessions, and reward yourself, you should learn more efficiently. Use these techniques over the next three or four years, gradually increasing your attention span so that you can study for a full hour without daydreaming.

**READ ACTIVELY.** When a study guide is not available, formulate and answer your own questions as you read. When using a study guide, follow the prepared exercises as outlined. With this study guide you are encouraged to find many of the answers yourself and write them into the area provided. This outline approach will help you develop this skill for courses without study guides.

**SET SMALL GOALS.** In the beginning do not expect yourself to read a complete chapter or finish an entire in chapter in your study guide in one study session. If you can do an entire chapter in one session, GREAT! But do not feel you have to. Set a goal of answering seven to ten questions and plan on taking a break when you have accomplished it. Over the next few years, gradually increase your goals.

**TAKE BREAKS FROM YOUR STUDY SESSIONS.** When you have answered or read the number of questions you set as a goal, take a break for 5-10 minutes. If you notice you are daydreaming a lot before you reach your goal, perhaps it was too large a step, and you should start out with a smaller one the next time. If you should discover you are daydreaming more than you are studying, *answer one more question* and take a 10 minute break. When you go back to studying, review the questions you have answered and then continue. You should strive to study at least 30 minutes for every 10 minute break.

**REWARD YOURSELF.** You will discover in *Chapter 7* of *Psychology* that research shows that behavior followed by reward tends to repeat itself. Of course earning a good grade, feeling proud of yourself, and having your teachers, family, and friends recognize your achievements are rewards, but why not go one step further? Make your hobbies, special activities, and favorite foods contingent (dependent) upon completion of your homework. The problem with self-reward is that it is easy to cheat. It is easy to watch a football game and plan to study afterward; but this can have a negative effect on your study habits. Instead, *always* plan your time so that reward comes *after* you study. This way you really will increase your studying and learning rates. The other way around (sports or computer games--and then studying) only increases your procrastination rate! Reset you priorities and reinforcement schedule.

## Memorization versus Understanding

Meaningful learning is much more permanent than rote learning (memorization). So, whenever you can, try to apply the concepts you are studying to your own experiences, look up words you are not familiar with, pay attention to examples given by your instructor if necessary. I have provided an enrichment glossary near the end of each chapter to assist your understanding of difficult words in *Psychology*. It is your responsibility to make everything you are trying to learn meaningful. Others can help you, but you will have to take the initiative to ask about any concepts giving you trouble.

In some cases memorization is an efficient way to help you recall information. This is so when you have made the information meaningful and are trying to remember names or lists of words. An effective way to memorize lists of material is to use mnemonic (nuh-MON-ik) devices. Mnemonic devices allow you to organize meaningless material into meaningful stories or words. In the textbook, *Chapter 8*, you will learn many interesting rudiments about human memory and forgetting. For example, if you wanted to remember the words cat, dish, punishment, nowhere, man, song, and gruesome you could create a story incorporating the word list. Try this: A *cat* was drinking milk from a *dish* when *punishment* fell upon him from *nowhere*. Turning his head the cat saw it was the *man* singing the *song* that had delivered the *gruesome* blow. Or if you wanted to remember the names Sabrina, Ulysses, Romeo, Pandora, Raina, Isis, Sebastian, and Ezekiel, you could simply remember the word SURPRISE. Mnemonic devices provide you with cues for recalling necessary information. You will find more about mnemonics and other memory strategies in *Chapter 8* of your *Psychology* text.

## DEVELOPING EFFECTIVE CLASSROOM BEHAVIORS

### Active Listening

Although entertainment, socializing with your peers, and conforming to the norms of going to college may be among your reasons for attending classroom lectures, one would hope that your primary reasons are to listen and learn. As with reading, to be a successful learner through listening you must be an active participant. Here are some tips that might help:

1. Exercise control over your thoughts by consciously directing your attention toward what is being said.
2. Allow the speaker's lead-in statements to act as cues that important information is about to be given. Lead-in statements will begin with phrases like "The main idea ...," "There are four approaches ...," "Another viewpoint ...," "In conclusion ...," and so on.
3. Silently ask yourself questions about what is being said and, as the lecture proceeds, try to answer them.
4. Ask questions in class, when the lecturer is ready for them, to clarify anything you missed or did not understand.
5. Try to make connections between what is being said now and what you recall from previous lectures or text material.

### Taking Notes

Listening and writing at the same time can be somewhat distracting. If you are listening actively and intently you may find it difficult to write down as much as you would like; if you are writing a lot down you may find yourself falling behind and missing parts of the lecture. For these reasons it is important to give some thought to your listening/note taking approach, and during the first few lectures of a course adapt your listening and note taking skills to the style and pace of the lecture.

As with reading and listening, note taking can become merely a passive activity. If your approach to note taking involves trying to write down, word for word, just about everything that the lecturer says, you will be more involved in getting words on paper than in focusing your attention and asking questions about what points are important. An effective approach for successful classroom learning is to be an active listener, take well-organized and brief yet explicit notes, making them complete enough to provide you with an overview of the entire lecture. Here are some ideas that may help you take good class lecture notes.

1. Use an 8 1/2" x 11" three-ring binder that allows you to add and remove pages. This will allow you to keep all of your notes in one place and in order.
2. Develop an outlining system that works well for you. Your outline of what is said in the lecture should reflect major ideas, minor points that follow those ideas, and the relationship between ideas. Complete sentences take time to write and, for the most part, are unnecessary. Try to catch the lecture ideas in short phrases that include key words.
3. Make some notation of all ideas brought out in the lecture, even those you have read about in the text or already know, so that you can be reminded of all the ideas the lecturer felt were important to the main lecture topic.

4.  Use multiple color highlighters to reflect your outline. Try different colors for major and minor points.

5.  If you are a "doodler," then turn your doodles into meaningful *icons* for emphasizing important material. Being a good student does not come naturally or easily for most. It takes self-discipline, realistic scheduling, and a true desire to succeed. The important thing to remember is that almost anyone who wants to be a good student can be.

# HOW TO USE GRADE AID

## HOW TO USE THIS STUDY GUIDE

You may want to think of your study guide as a "How to Do It" manual or a carefully tested "recipe" that will help you succeed in your psychology class. As you work with it over the next few months and through practice come to understand its purpose, you will probably find yourself using the formula it provides in most of your other classes, too. *Grade Aid* is designed to compliment Lefton and Brannon's *Psychology, Eighth Edition*. It will assist you in learning the essential terms, concepts, theories, and important research in the field of psychology. It is not meant as a substitute for *Psychology,* but rather as an adjunct to your learning process.

## BEFORE YOU READ...

At the beginning of each study guide chapter, you will find a brief summary of the chapter. Research studies on learning and memory have shown it is much easier to learn if you have some idea of the topic and the specific areas you will be learning. Having an overview prepares you for what is about to be read and gives you a glimpse into the exciting topics you are about to learn.

## CHAPTER OBJECTIVES

"When you have mastered the material in this chapter you will be able to ...." The chapter learning objectives serve four purposes: first, they tell you specifically what you should expect to know when you have completed studying the chapter; second, they give you an overview of what is in the chapter; third, they provide cues when you begin to review the chapter in order to prepare for a test; and fourth, they can be used as practice essay questions.

## AS YOU READ

People, terms, concepts, and ideas will be presented throughout this section in a variety of formats. These exercises will be a good indicator of how quickly you are getting the information. The exercises in *Grade Aid Study Guide* will allow you to test your understanding by applying the text's psychology concepts to new situations. If you can transfer your textbook knowledge successfully to these examples, what you are learning is taking on meaning. Meaningful learning is much more permanent than simple memorization. Other ways that you can make the things you are learning meaningful include doing your best to apply the concepts you are studying to your own experiences, looking up unfamiliar words, and paying attention to examples given in your text.

## AFTER YOU READ...THE SELF-TESTS

At the conclusion of each chapter you will be provided a chapter Self-Test. The self-tests will give you immediate feedback on how well you have learned. If you miss more than one or two questions on the self-test you need to study the chapter lessons more thoroughly. If you are preparing for a comprehensive exam in your course, you can combine chapter tests to simulate a real course exam. It has been my experience that providing students with a sample of what a test will be like in their course relieves much of the pre-test anxiety and allows them to concentrate on the material in a much more efficient manner. Essay questions are also provided for better course exam preparation. Combine the two for a real assessment of your learning.

## TERM IDENTIFICATION

College students who speak English as a second language reviewed the textbook and circled words they did not understand. These words have been compiled in the Term Identification at the end of each chapter.

   *Grade Aid* was written with the student in mind. I welcome your comments, opinions, and suggestions for future editions. My address is Andrew H. Ryan, Jr. Ph.D. c/o Psychology Department, University of South Carolina, Columbia, SC 29208 or my E-Mail/internet address is AHRyanJR@hotmail.com.

# EXAM PREPARATION

# HOW TO PASS YOUR EXAMS

**FACING EXAMS.** I have questioned thousands of my students about using study guides and what features they like the most. Students dread preparing for exams and suggest to me thousands of grading methods that do not include taking exams. However, students recognize that the most prevalent method of assessing acquired knowledge is to administer exams. Test anxiety can interfere with your ability to learn, as well as with accuracy of recall during the exam itself. There are a number of methods to relieve you of test-anxiety. They all have one common goal--*to help you be relaxed and confident going into the exam.* Many students in survey-type courses find that the amount of material requires many more hours of study than they had anticipated, thus, many more hours of exam preparation. Students also feel that preparing for an exam covering several chapters is anxiety provoking, and they come to the exam with a great deal of tension. Achieving top scores on exams requires preparation and practice. One way of mitigating the tension is to give the student a chance to simulate the exam without the pressure of failing or the shock of a tough question causing the student to block on the correct answer. This Exam Preparation Section is designed to provide you practice exams in a tension-free environment and prepare you for the real thing.

**PREPARING FOR EXAMS.** Preparing for exams should be an ongoing process. As you read your text, listen in class, and take lecture notes, keep in mind--an exam is coming. Then, about one week before an exam, begin your study sessions. Do not wait until the day before because time pressure, low energy, and unexpected events are too likely to interfere with your ability to prepare well. About a week before the exam you should take the following steps:

1. Ask your instructor what the exam will cover, what material will be omitted, and what kinds of questions will be used.
2. Make a list of things you must know and rank them according to their importance. You will want to give the most important and difficult concepts more preparation time.
3. Spend some time predicting test questions: How might they be worded? How general or detailed might they be? How might two or more concepts be combined into one question?
4. Begin reviewing. Your text, lecture notes, *study guide questions and answers, chapter learning objectives, practice tests,* and *self-test* will become extremely useful tools at this time.
5. Schedule group study sessions with other students. Sharing ideas about what might be covered on the test and talking out loud about the things you have learned will help clarify and solidify your understanding.
6. Make up practice exams and test yourself before the test day. If you don't know it all yet you still have time to get the answers or clarification from your instructor.

**ANSWERING ESSAY TEST QUESTIONS.** Essay test questions require that you know the material well enough to be able to recall from memory, in an organized way, both major and minor points that will provide an answer. The *Self Tests* in this study guide will let you know if you have grasped the concepts beyond rote memorization. When presented with an essay test, keep these steps in mind.

1. Before you begin to answer any test questions, read all of the questions and make some quick notes about the major and minor points you will want to cover when answering them.
2. Estimate how much time you should give to each question and try to stick to your schedule. You will want to allow more time for difficult questions and questions that carry more points toward scoring of the test. If possible, plan to have some time in the last minutes of the class session to review and polish your answers.
3. Answer the easier questions first.
4. Answer each question as directly as possible and avoid wandering and writing too much or too little.
5. Leave a few blank lines between answers so that you can go back if time allows and add ideas.

**ANSWERING OBJECTIVE TEST QUESTIONS.** Objective test questions include multiple-choice, true-false, and matching questions. These questions require you to recognize and discriminate between correct and incorrect answers. The *Self-Tests* at the end of each chapter, should give you good practice at this. When taking an objective test keep the following in mind.

1. Read each question carefully and completely; do not jump to conclusions and assume that you have the correct answer until you have read and considered the entire question.
2. Give careful thought to questions that include words such as *always, never, all, tendency,* or *sometimes.* The first three terms may indicate that the statement is too extreme and perhaps false; the last two terms show more qualified conditions, suggesting that the statement may be true; however, these rules are not absolute.
3. Treat each alternative in a multiple-choice question as a true-false statement. Eliminate those alternatives that are definitely false and if more than one answer seems to be true, choose the one that most thoroughly and directly answers the question.
4. Do not spend too much time on any one question. If you are unsure of an answer, put a check mark in the margin next to the question and go back to it later.
5. The rule of thumb about changing answers is to stick with your original answer unless you have *strong* second thoughts about it. If you feel reasonably sure that your second thoughts are correct then go ahead and change the answer.

**SIMULATING YOUR EXAMS.** You can prepare better for your course examinations if you follow a couple of proven review steps. First, in *Psychology* you are presented with a new glossary of terminology. In the *Term Identification Section* you are provided with a list of new or difficult terms and asked to create *Flash Cards* to enhance your memory for these *Psychology* terms. This technique is a proven way to increase your ability to recall the correct test answer in many test formats such as matching or short answer type questions. The next, more difficult task is to recognize the correct answer when you are given less than the complete definition, as in multiple-choice items or scenarios, where the item stem is lengthy, and you need to determine what the salient points are before attempting to answer. What if you could be given bits of information about specific topics and asked to correctly identify and spell the topic? What if you could learn difficult concepts, increase your confidence and also have some fun doing it? I have provided a sample of multiple-choice test items similar in content to the items your instructor may choose for your exam. These *Self Tests* items are real and an excellent method of practicing for an exam.

Although Lefton and Brannon's *Psychology,* Eighth Edition is written in a very logical format, many instructors choose to alter the chapter sequence to better fit individual instructor goals. Preparing for a multiple chapter exam is difficult, but there is a way to put together your own practice exam and build your confidence prior to the real exam. For example, if your instructor assigns Chapters 1, 2 and 5 as the readings covered on the next exam, you would use your *Flash Cards* for Chapters 1, 2, and 5; then remove the *Self Tests* for Chapters 1, 2, and 5 and combine them to make a simulated exam covering the same material as your instructor's exam. You can mix and match the cards, and tests in any way you choose. Combine them in whatever fashion most closely resembles your real exam. Be sure to grade yourself on the simulated exam and keep up with how this practice helps you on the real exam. If you feel like you need to practice more than once, simply make copies of the pages before you begin, and scramble them for subsequent practice exams.

After creating your own simulated exams, you may also want to test your knowledge by taking the sample exams provided via the internet. The *Lefton Learning Community* an internet resource for *Psychology*, Eighth Edition is located at www.ablongman.com/lefton. **Check it out!**

# Chapter 1

# What is Psychology?

# Before you read...

Students are introduced to the science of psychology. Since psychology is a science, adherence to the principles of scientific endeavor is critical. The scientific method is divided into five basic steps and each is outlined as it relates to research.

Lefton and Brannon continues by defining such terms as *variables*, *hypotheses*, *experimental* and *control groups*, *sample*, and what it means to say there is a significant difference. One of the skills that psychologists need is the ability to think critically. Lefton and Brannon asks students to become critical thinkers to better understand and evaluate research and its findings.

In conducting effective research that will be generalizable, one must also attend to the many elements of a diverse society such as that of the United States. Ethnocentrism and its impact on psychology is discussed. Also, the ethics of psychological research are discussed in relation to the necessity of animal research and the use of deception in human research.

Chapter 1 continues with a look at the brief history of the science of psychology and its evolution over the past 100 plus years. An overview of how schools of psychological thought such as structuralism, functionalism, Gestalt psychology, and psychoanalysis, have expanded into the more modern schools of behaviorism, humanistic psychology, cognitive psychology, biological perspectives, and the evolutionary perspective.

Psychologist/psychiatrist, what's the difference? The profession of psychology is diverse and has a number of educational requirements and specialty areas just as in medicine. Lefton and Brannon describes the differences between psychologists, psychiatrists, and other professionals practicing psychology. The areas of applied research, human services, and experimental psychology are explained, and the subfields that encompass these exciting careers are examined.

The science of psychology is as diverse as the behaviors and mental processes it seeks to understand. Chapter 1, like the discipline itself, is meant to give a broad understanding of this diversity and open your mind to the methods and procedures used by psychologist. Lefton and Brannon provides a broad base from which the rest of the text will develop in taking you on this fascinating journey through *Psychology*.

# Chapter Objectives

After reading this chapter, you should be able to:

- Explain how psychologists discover the underpinnings of human behavior and mental processes through the conduct of empirical research.
- Define Neuroanatomy, describe how nature and nurture interact and how culture impacts behavior.
- Understand and describe the two-way interaction between biology and the environment that shapes peoples' behavior.
- Summarize the three principles that form the core of psychology.
- Identify and describe the five basic steps of the scientific method.
- Define the key elements of research, *independent variable*, *dependent variable*, *hypotheses*, and *control group* and explain the importance of each to the research process.
- State how you can use critical thinking skills to evaluate research.
- Identify factors that contribute to human diversity and explain why universal statements about human behavior are not always true.
- Describe how human participants in research experiments are safeguarded by ethics. Discuss the use of deception in psychological research and two conditions that must be met when deception is used.
- Explain why animals are used in research and how they are safeguarded by ethics.
- Define what it means to describe something as a school of psychological thought. Then compare and contrast structuralism, functionalism, Gestalt psychology, and psychoanalysis.
- Define behaviorism, humanistic psychology, cognitive psychology, and the biological perspective. Include the similarities and differences between them and describe eclecticism.
- Describe the Evolutionary and Biopsychology perspectives.
- Define Clinical psychologists, Counseling Psychologists and Psychiatrists. Describe applied research, human services, and experimental psychology and characterize the subfields of each.
- Identify how psychologists are trained and possible career fields
- Discuss career opportunities in psychology. Then discuss the impact of the increasing numbers of women and ethnic minorities who are entering the field.

# As you read...

## Four Recurring Themes in Psychology

1. What are the 4 organizing themes in psychology?

2. What is the focus of many current brain studies?

3. Our _____ and our _____ combine to form our human behavior.

## What is This Science of Psychology

1. How does the author define psychology?

2. Define Empiricism?

3. A theory is a collection of interrelated ideas and facts put forward to _____ and _____ behavior.

4. Psychology is the science of behavior and _____.

---

**1-1.  Three Principles of Scientific Endeavor**

5. List the 3 principles that are the core of psychology.

    1. _____

    2. _____

    3. _____

6. Give an example of bias in psychological research.

**1-2. The Scientific Method in Psychology**

7. Give the 5 Basic Steps of the Scientific Method.

8. Identify the independent and dependent variables in each of the following experiments.

A psychologist investigates the effects that level of background noise has on the time it takes subjects to complete a series of analytical problems.
> Independent_____
> Dependent_____

A researcher conducts a study in which she measures academic performance among students who do not eat breakfast regularly.
> Independent_____
> Dependent_____

Hospitalized schizophrenics are rewarded for cooperative behaviors, and a clinical psychologist observes to see if their rate of being cooperative increases as a result.
> Independent_____
> Dependent_____

9. What are extraneous variables?

10. Describe what a hypothesis is and give an example.

11. Define experimental and control groups.

12. What are significant differences? How do they impact scientific research?

---

**1-7. The Research Process: To Sleep, Perchance to Experiment**

---

## Matching

1. ____Variables
2. ____Hypothesis
3. ____Sample
4. ____Correlation
5. ____Objectivity
6. ____Replication
7. ____Participant

   a) previously known as the subject of an experiment; one whose behavior is observed for data collection
   b) educated guess
   c) repeating an experiment to verify results
   d) events not necessarily causally relative
   e) group that is assumed to represent the population
   f) a condition or characteristic of a situation or person
   g) evaluating research without preconceived ideas

## Critical Thinking: An Active Learning Process

1. How can critical thinking be applied to evaluate research?

## Avoiding Ethnocentrism and Other Forms of Bias

1. Define Ethnocentrism and give an example.

2. How does ethnocentrism lead to institutional racism?

3. Compare and contrast race and ethnicity.

4. Why should psychologists study ethnicity over race?

5. The United States is a _____ culture while many Asian countries have a _____ culture.

6. When it comes to understanding diversity, we need to realize that there are usually more differences _____ a group than between groups.

# Ethics in Psychological Research

1.    List 3 things an informed consent includes

    1. _____

    2. _____

    3. _____

2.    Discuss the use of deception in psychological research.

## 1-8.  Point/Counterpoint: Nonhuman Animals in Research

3.    Why animals are used in research?

4.    What advantages are there in conducting research on animals?

# Psychology: A Young Discipline

## 1-9.  The Early Traditions

1.    Define what it means to describe something as a school of psychological thought.

2.    Compare and contrast structuralism, functionalism, and Gestalt psychology.

3.    Analyzing and describing thoughts as they occur is called _____.

## 1-10.  From Past to Present

4.    Define psychoanalysis, behaviorism, humanistic psychology, cognitive psychology, and the biological perspective.

5.    Include the similarities and differences between them.

6.    List 4 aspects of self-actualization

        1. _____

        2. _____

        3. _____

        4. _____


7.    Fill in the missing information that describes the perspectives on psychological issues.

| Perspective | Main idea |
|---|---|
| Psychoalanlysis | Maladjustment is a consequence of anxiety resulting from unresolved conflict |
|  | Uniqueness of each human being's experience is central as is the idea that human beings have free will to determine their destiny |
|  | Describes and measures observable behaviors |
| Cognitive |  |
| Behaviorism |  |
|  | Explains behavior by analyzing how specific behaviors have led to adaptations |
|  | Examines psychology in light of how physical mechanisms affect emotions, feelings, thoughts, desires and sensory processes. |
|  | Allows the researcher to view behavior from diverse orientations and from a client's perspective |

**1-11.  Today's Perspectives**

8.      Describe the Evolutionary and Biopsychology Perspectives

# Who Are These People Called Psychologists?

1.      What are the differences between a Clinical Psychologist, Counseling Psychologist, and Psychiatrists.

2.      What is a psychoanalyst?

**1-12.  What Psychologists Do**

3.      Describe applied research, human services, and experimental psychology.

4.      Experimental psychologists use a set of _____, to examine a wide variety of topics.

**1-13.  Making Psychology a Career**

5.      Discuss career opportunities in psychology.

6.      Identify how psychologists are trained.

**1-14. The Changing Face of Psychology**

7.      What is the impact of the increasing number of women and minorities entering the field?

Psychology
Empiricism
Theory
Scientific Method
Hypothesis
Experiment
Variable
Independent Variable
Dependent Variable
Participant
Experimental Group
Control Group
Sample
Significant Difference
Ethnocentrism
Ethics
Informed Consent
Debriefing
Operational Definition

Structuralism
Introspection
Functionalism
Gestalt
Psychoanalytic
Humanistic Psychology
Self-Actualization
Behaviorism
Cognitive Psychology
Biopsychology Perspective
Evolutionary Psychology
Neuroscience Perspective
Psychologist
Clinical Psychologist
Psychiatrist
Psychoanalyst

# After you read . . . Self Test

## Chapter 1 Self Test

1.  Psychology can be defined as the study of: (4)
    A.  humans and other animals.
    B.  stimulus and responses.
    C.  behavior and mental processes.
    D.  none of the above

2.  Who founded the school of structuralism and the first psychological laboratory? (19)
    A.  Sigmund Freud
    B.  Ivan Pavlov
    C.  John Watson
    D.  Wilhelm Wundt

3.  Empiricism is the view that knowledge should be acquired through (6)
    A.  Observation
    B.  Logic
    C.  Intuition
    D.  Personal experiences

4.  The focus of John B. Watson's research was: (22)
    A.  the basic elements of consciousness.
    B.  stream of consciousness.
    C.  observable behaviors.
    D.  the useful functions of the mind.

5.  Humanistic psychology is *not* associated with: (22)
    A.  uniqueness.
    B.  the unconscious mind.
    C.  free will.
    D.  Abraham Maslow.

6.  A set of procedures that specifies exactly how a particular variable is to be measured is called a(n)  (9)
    A.  operational definition
    B.  experimental document
    C.  subjectivity report
    D.  hypothetical statement

7.  Critical Thinking involves all of the following *except*: (11)
    A.  evaluating evidence
    B.  ignoring biases
    C.  assessing outcomes
    D.  looking for repeatable results

8.  Which variable causes changes in the behavior being studied? (9)
A.   dependent
B.   random
C.   control
D.   independent

9.  In an experiment *only* the experimental group  (10)
A.   is given an informed consent
B.   receives the treatment
C.   must represent the population being studied
D.   is debriefed

10.  The biopsychology perspective does *not* looks at (24-25)
A.   introspection.
B.   central nervous system problems
C.   how behavior changes brain structure and function
D.   genetic abnormalities

11.  Ethinic minorities comprise _____% of APA membership and African Americans and Hispanics receive about _____% of the new PhDs in psychology each year. (31)
A.   14.8 , 66
B.   28, 5
C.   73,50
D.   6, 32

12.  Theories are (6)
A.   rarely used in psychology
B.   used to describe, explain and predict behavior
C.   not formed from empirical observations
D.   used to test hypothesis

13.  A factor in an experiment that might affect the results but is not of interest to the experimenter is called a(n) (10)
A.   hypothesis
B.   extraneous variable.
C.   replication.
D.   theoretical condition.

14.  Compared to a psychiatrist, a clinical psychologist's training makes him or her better prepared to (27)
A.   engage in research about psychological problems.
B.   prescribe the appropriate medications for a patient.
C.   understand the biological causes of disorders.
D.   explain psychological disorders to their patients.

15. Of the basic scientific principles, skepticism implies scientist should (7)
A.    describe and predict future behavior
B.    collect information from small samples of people
C.    develop new theories
D.    wait for replication of results

16. A condition or characteristic of a situation or person that can change over time or that can be different between different situations or people is called a(n) (8)
A.    variable.
B.    hypothesis.
C.    correlation.
D.    experiment.

17. Functionalism is *not* associated with (20)
A.    William James
B.    adaptation to the environment
C.    consciousness
D.    Titchener

18. Which of these is an important reason for using animals as research subjects in psychology? (18)
A.    Their short life spans make it easier to study changes over several generations.
B.    There are no ethical rules that limit what research can be performed with animals.
C.    Their mental processes are practically identical with those of humans.
D.    Animals don't feel pain, loneliness, or stress the same way humans do.

19. When a researcher uses deception as part of a research project, it is especially important that there should be (17-18)
A.    no animals or children used in the research.
B.    both informed consent and debriefing.
C.    a second piece of research that does not use deception.
D.    a careful record of all responses.

20. Cognitive psychology is a school of psychological thought that emphasizes the importance of (23)
A.    biological and chemical processes in the brain.
B.    measuring overt, observable behaviors.
C.    mental processes such as thought and memory.
D.    unresolved conflicts and forces in the unconscious.

21. Which of the following is NOT one of the five research criteria that may guide critical thinking? (11)
A.    methodology
B.    participants
C.    publishability
D.    conclusions

22. _____ is not a principle of scientific endeavor. (6)

A. Accuracy
B. Hypothesis development
C. Objectivity
D. Healthy skepticism

23. In an experiment, the _____ variable is manipulated by the experimenter and the _____ variable is expected to change due to the manipulation. (9)
A. dependent, extraneous
B. extraneous, independent
C. independent, dependent
D. dependent, independent

24. A significant difference is a difference (10-11)
A. that is due to chance
B. can be inferred to be due to the manipulation of variables
C. researchers ignore
D. are not used to confirm the hypothesis

25. A(n) _____ is conducted at the conclusion of the experiment and serves to inform the participant as to the true nature of the study. (17)
A. informed consent
B. demand characteristic
C. self-fulfilling prophecy
D. debriefing

26. A medical doctor who has chosen to devote their efforts to the treatment of emotional or mental disorders is known as a _____. (27)
A. clinical psychologist
B. psychiatrist
C. counseling psychologist
D. psychoanalyst

27. The steps of the scientific method do *not* include (7)
A. forming a hypothesis
B. collecting and analyzing data
C. stating the problem
D. ignoring results

28. Individuals in the fields of engineering, educational, forensic, and industrial/organizational psychology demonstrate skills in _____ psychology. (28)
A. applied
B. human service
C. experimental
D. health

29. _____ was a school of psychological thought that was based on the premise that it was insufficient to examine the individual parts of the human mind and/or behavior, but that it was necessary to examine the total experience of the individual. (20)
A.     Structuralism
B.     Functionalism
C.     Gestaltism
D.     Behaviorism

30. _____ is a field of psychology that examines the mental processes involved in behavior, which are viewed as key components not included in the approach of _____. (22-23)
A.     Cognitive psychology, behaviorism
B.     Evolutionary psychology, cognitive psychology
C.     Cognitive psychology, humanistic psychology
D.     Biological psychology, behaviorism

31. Structuralism was an early school of psychological thought that emphasized (19)
A.     the organization of immediate, conscious thought
B.     the study of overt, measurable behavior
C.     the importance of the unconscious mind
D.     the use of complex mathematical analyses

32. Behaviorism is primarily concerned with: (22)
A.     how behavior is learned and how it can be modified.
B.     unconscious influences of early childhood experience.
C.     inherited characteristics.
D.     fulfillment of the human potential.

33. All of the following comparisons between clinical psychologists and psychiatrists are true *except*: (26-27)
A.     both can now prescribe medications.
B.     Both see a similar mix of clients.
C.     Clinical psychologists generally have more extensive training in assessment than do psychiatrists.
D.     Both see abnormal behavior as a disease.

34. People who choose psychology as a career can expect: (30)
A.     salaries ranging from $500,000 to $1,000,000 annually.
B.     to find a wide variety of job opportunities.
C.     some difficulty finding a job since employment opportunities have recently stabilized.
D.     all of the above

35. _____promoted Structuralism in the United States while _____ promoted Functionalism  (19-20)
A.      Titchner; James
B.      Wundt;Titchner
C.      James; Titchner
D.      Wertheimer; Kofka

36. In the field of humanistic psychology, each person's desire to fulfill his or her personal potential is called (22-23)
A.      self-actualization
B.      psychoanalysis
C.      cognitive development
D.      behavioral control

37. A correlation: (9)
A.      exists when two events are regularly associated with one another.
B.      means a change in one variable causes a change in another variable.
C.      is found only through controlled laboratory experiments.
D.      is an experimental variable.

38. A tentative statement expressing a causal relationship between two events that will be evaluated in a research study is called: (7-8)
A.      an operational definition.
B.      a theory.
C.      a hypothesis.
D.      a variable.

39. Ethnicity is (14)
A.      something you are born with
B.      learned from friends, family and experiences
C.      not important to psychological research
D.      none of the above

40. Introspection is (19-20)
A.      used by behaviorists
B.      involves describing and analyzing thoughts as they occur
C.      is part of the cognitive revolution
D.      was developed by Koffka

41. When psychologists consider factors such as ethnicity, gender, socioeconomic class, religion they are investigating: (17)
A.      structuralism.
B.      dependent variables.
C.      random assignment of subjects.
D.      human diversity.

42. The psychoanalytic approach (21-22)
A. was created by Freud
B. deals with the unconscious mind
C. assumes emotional problems are the result of unresolved conflicts
D. all of the above

43. The fields of counseling and clinical psychologists (27)
A. have responsibilities that are converging
B. cover completely different types of problems
C. are both decreasing in popularity
D. would not deal with the problem of spousal abuse

44. Which of the following is NOT an overt action that psychology would study? (6)
A. feelings of anger
B. kissing
C. facial expressions
D. changes in brain waves.

45. All of the following contribute to research bias EXCEPT (5)
A. age
B. culture
C. gender
D. none of the above

# When You Have Finished

## Essay Questions

1. Define and describe the independent and dependent variables in an experiment looking at the effects of culture on alcohol consumption. (8-9)

2. Give a brief history and description of the early schools of thought in psychology. Be sure to include the people associated which each school of thought. (19-21)

3. A person starts to eat everyday at noon, how would a behaviorist describe this behavior, how would a cognitive psychologist describe this behavior? (22-23)

4. Is animal research necessary and ethical? Give arguments for both sides. (18)

5. Compare and contrast how a Clinical Psychologist and a Psychiatrist would treat an individual with depression. (26-27)

# Chapter 2

# Neuroscience: The Brain and Behavior

## Before you read...

You learned in Chapter 1 that psychology is the study of behavior and mental processes. All behavior as well as mental processes originate in the biological systems of our body. In Chapter 2, Lefton and Brannon explain the importance of genetics and its contribution to behavior and mental processes. Studies of genetic defects and twins provide insight into the nature versus nurture controversy.

Communication in the nervous system is complex and difficult to grasp in its entirety at first. Therefore, Chapter 2 breaks the nervous system down into its basic units and begins by explaining how the electrochemical process works. Beginning with the neuron, the authors describe the journey of a neural impulse from one neuron to another and how neurotransmitters may hold the key to understanding specific human behaviors such as drug addiction.

The nervous system is composed of two subsystems, the central nervous system (CNS) and the peripheral nervous system (PNS). Working concurrently these two subsystems send, receive, process, interpret, and store neuronal information. The brain, which is a component of the CNS, is divided into three sections: hindbrain, midbrain, and forebrain. Several functions of these sections are described including how specific functions are linked to behavior.

Monitoring neuronal activity has progressed from measuring head size in the 18th century to using high-tech CAT, PET, and MRI technology to scan brain tissue and its processes more precisely and provide valuable information about the workings of the brain and nervous system. Other important attributes such as brain specialization, and plasticity are discussed to provide an understanding of the development of the brain in individual humans.

In conclusion Chapter 2 discusses the contribution of the endocrine system and its production of hormones to human behavior. Lefton and Brannon refer to the pituitary gland as the master gland because of its role in regulating the adrenal gland and the pancreas in hormonal production. The question of gender differences being caused by brain structure or hormones is discussed.

Understanding the basics of biology and behavior will go a long way toward helping you in later chapters of *Psychology*. Chapter 2 provides the basics that Lefton and Brannon will expand on in the rest of the text.

# Chapter Objectives

- Understand the difference between nature and nurture and how each affects the expression of human traits.

- Understand the basic components of genetics including genes, chromosomes, genotype and phenotype.

- Be able to explain that correlation is not causation.

- What is the evolutionary approach to psychology and how is it applied.

- Review communication in the nervous system by specifying the three types of neurons, the parts of a neuron, and the electrochemical process.

- Outline how the study of neuro-transmitters has led scientists to a better understanding of the relationship between neurotransmitters and behavior.

- Be able to describe the peripheral nervous system and its subsystems.

- Identify and describe the structures of the central nervous system.

- Understand the five principles governing brain organization.

- Examine the structure and functions of the brain including the substructures of the hindbrain, midbrain, and forebrain.

- Specify how modern techniques such as CAT, PET, and MRI and fMRI scans are making the examination of brain processes more precise.

- Understand brain specialization and some of the research that has been conducted.

- Examine how the plasticity of the brain may be modified and fine tuned through such things as experience and drugs, and how plasticity gives hope to altering the effects of neuronal disease.

- Examine how the endocrine system and the various endocrine glands are related to sexual behavior, energy levels, human growth and development, and reactions to stress.

- Use your critical thinking skills to interpret how brain structure and/or hormones contribute to gender differences in human performance.

# As you read...

## Genetics and Evolutionary Psychology

1.    Define Genetics


2.    If a trait is 30%_____, then 30% of the differences among a group of people can be attributed to _____.


| 2-1    Nature and Nurture |
|---|

3.    Define the terms nature and nurture.


4.    Discuss how both nature and nurture affects the expression of human traits.


5.    Label each of the following statements as being primarily the product of nature, nurture, or both nature and nurture.  Remember, all behavior is ultimately the product of both.  However, the statements below *emphasize* (in some cases) nature or nurture.  They are designed only to give you practice in discriminating between the two components of behavior.  If you cannot determine a *primary* influence, "both" is probably the correct answer.

   A.    _____ Unlike most babies, at the age of seven months, Mario said his first word in the language he had been exposed to by his parents.

   B.    _____ Mary has blond hair and is very tall.

   C.    _____ Having lived in China, France, and Italy, Kim can prepare Chinese, French, and Italian meals.

   D.    _____ Donna's level of dopamine is so low that her body trembles most of the time.

   E.    _____ By the age of twelve, Francis was mastering college-level academic material.


| 2-2    The Basics of Genetics |
|---|

6.    What are Genes?


7.    What are Chromosomes?

8.　State the differences between a dominant and recessive traits.


9.　A _____ is a person's genetic make-up. A _____ is a person's observable characteristics.


10.　Unexpected changes in gene replication are called _____.


| 2-3 | **Mapping the Genome** |
| --- | --- |

11.　What is the human genome?


12.　What ethical questions does the mapping of the human genome raise?


***Brain and Behavior: The Special Case of Twins***

13.　Discuss how twin studies have revealed information about the contribution of nature and nurture to human behavior.


| 2-4 | **Each Human Being is Unique** |
| --- | --- |

14.　Describe how the field of behavioral genetics uses an understanding of basic biological mechanisms and their relationships to explain behavior.


15.　Define Multigenic.


***The Research Process: Correlation is Not Causation***

16.　Compare cause-and-effect relationships to correlated events.


17.　A _____ is a number that expresses the degree and direction of a relationship of two variables.

**The Evolutionary Approach to Psychology**

18.   What is Evolutionary Psychology?


19.   Define Natural Selection.


20.   _____ has occurred when a trait or inherited characteristic has increased in a population.

   *Point/Counterpoint: Are Men Naturally Promiscuous?*


21.   Is there an evolutionary basis for differences in sexual behavior?


# Communication and the Nervous System

**2-6     The Neuron**

1.   What is a neuron?


2.   Define and compare afferent neurons and efferent neurons.


3.   What are the 3 types of neurons?


4.   _____ _____(s)  provide nourishment and structure to neurons.


5.   What is a myelin sheath and how does it help neurons?


6.   List the 4 primary parts of a neuron.


7.   Explain the electrochemical process.

# Matching

1) _____ Action Potential
2) _____ Axon
3) _____ Central Nervous System
4) _____ Dendrite
5) _____ Neuron
6) _____ Refractory Period
7) _____ Synapse

a) the basic unit of the nervous system
b) fibers extending from the neuron cell body and receive signals from neighboring cells
c) small space between neurons
d) brain and spinal cord
e) transmits signals from cell body through axon terminal to adjacent neurons
f) the time a neuron needs to recover after firing
g) an electrical current that travels down the axon of a neuron

## 2-7    Neurotransmitters and Behavior

8.    What is a neurotransmitter?

9.    Compare and contrast EPSP and IPSP

10.    List 3 neurotransmitters and how they effect behavior

11.    _____ is a neuropeptide that inhibits certain synaptic transmissions involving pain.

12.    Define psychopharmacology.

13.    Define agonists and antagonists.

# Organization of the Nervous System

1. What are the function and structures of the Peripheral Nervous System

2. List and describe the two subsystems of the peripheral nervous system.

3. Compare and Contrast the sympathetic and parasympathetic nervous systems.

4. Identify the nervous system (central, somatic, parasympathetic, or sympathetic) that is most specifically illustrated by each of the following situations.

    A. _____ In an effort to shape up, John engages in a series of sit-ups and push-ups.

    B. _____ Mary, while walking to her psychology class, comes across a large dog who growls at her. Mary notices her heart beating faster and her breathing increased.

    C. _____ Jane just moved off-campus and must draw up a new budget. She carefully analyzes her assets, her bills, and how she would like to spend the excess after bills.

    D. _____ An increase in the secretion of digestive juices and blood flowing to the gastrointestinal system causes the meal Simon just ate to break down into protein and carbohydrate molecules and nutrients that are eventually absorbed by his blood system.

| 2-9 | The Central Nervous System |

5. What is the function of the Central Nervous System?

6. List and describe the structures of the Central Nervous System.

# Brain Organization

## 2-10    Five Principles Governing Brain Organization

1.  What are the five key operating principles of the brain?

## 2-11    The Brain is Composed of Three Main Divisions

2.    What are the 3 main divisions of the brain?

## 2-12    Hindbrain and Midbrain

3.    What functions does the hindbrain perform?

4.    List and describe the 4 parts of the hindbrain.

5.    What are the functions of the midbrain?

## 2-13    Forebrain

6.    What are the functions and characteristics of the forebrain?

7.    Describe the functions of the thalamus and hypothalamus.

8.    Define cortex

9.    The cortex contains _____ that increase its surface area.

10.    List the 4 lobes of the cortex and their locations.

11.    What is the limbic system involved in?  What structures does it include?

12.    _____ is involved in navigating about the world, learning, and memory.

13.  _____ is involved in emotional behaviors.

14.  Give the location and function of the basal ganglia and corpus callosum.


# The Brain at Work

## 2-14    Monitoring Neuronal Activity

1.  List and describe 5 techniques to measure neural function.

2.  When people are relaxed, awake, and not actively thinking, their EEG is predominately composed of _____ _____.

3.  When a person is excited their EEG is predominately composed of _____ _____.

4.  _____ _____ _____ induces lesion-like disruptions in the brain allowing researchers to study attention, plasticity and discrimination.

5.  How are imaging techniques currently being used?


## 2-15    Brain Specialization- The Left and Right of Things

6.     Discuss the types of research that have been influential in developing our understanding of brain specialization.

7.     Discuss gender differences in the brain.

## 2-16    Plasticity and Change

8.     Define malleable and plasticity. Does the brain demonstrate both of these properties?

9.     When is neural plasticity the greatest?

# Hormones and Glands

1. Define hormones and compare them to neurotransmitters.


2. What are endocrine glands and give an example.


3. Why is the pituitary gland often called the body's master gland?


4. Complete the following table on the endocrine system.

| ENDOCRINE GLAND | HORMONE | EFFECT |
| --- | --- | --- |
|  | steroid hormones |  |
| pancreas |  |  |
|  | epinephrine (adrenaline) |  |

**Term Identification: Make flashcards for each of the following terms. Hint: Use the definitions in the margins of the chapter**

Genetics
Heritability
Nature
Nurture
Chromosome
Genes
Genotype
Pheontype
Mutations
Genome
Genetic Mapping
Identical Twins
Fraternal Twins
Correlation Coefficient
Evolutionary Psychology
Natural Selection
Adaptation
Nervous system
Neuron
Afferent neuron
Efferent neuron
Dendrites
Axon
Synapse
Action Potential
All-or-None
Refractory Period
Neurotransmitter
Agonist
Antagonist
Peripheral Nervous System

Somatic Nervous System
Autonomic Nervous System
Sympathetic Nervous System
Parasympathetic Nervous System
Central Nervous System
Spinal Cord
Brain
Hindbrain
Medulla
Pons
Cerebellum
Midbrain
Forebrain
Thalamus
Hypothalamus
Limbic System
Cortex
Convolutions
Electroencephalogram (EEG)
CT Scans
PET
MRI
fMRI
Split-Brain Patient
Endocrine Glands
Hormones
Pituitary Gland
Insulin
Diabetes Mellitus
Hypoglycemia

# After you read . . . Self Test

## Chapter 2 Self Test

1. The term *nature* refers to: (38)
    A. life's experiences.
    B. heredity.
    C. personality.
    D. the environment.

2. In response to the nature verses nurture debate, most psychologists agree that: (38)
    A. heredity is more important than environment.
    B. environment is more important than heredity.
    C. ultimately, all behavior is the result of the environment.
    D. both heredity and environment are important, but the question of which is more important has not been resolved.

3. Genes are: (39)
    A. the units of heredity transmission consisting of DNA and protein.
    B. strands of genetic material.
    C. used to describe the development of twins.
    D. found only in ova and sperm sex cells.

4. Twins make good subjects for studying the relative effects of nature-nurture because they: (41)
    A. begin life in the same uterine environment.
    B. are easier to track over time.
    C. have the same life experiences.
    D. inherited chromosomes from their parents.

5. Twin and adoption studies have shown that intellectual abilities: (41)
    A. depend entirely on nature.
    B. are primarily a result of nurture.
    C. are the result of an interaction of inherited traits and family environment.
    D. usually get better as a person matures.

6. The _____ of the neuron has thin branching fibers and receives information from neighboring neurons. (47)
    A. cell body
    B. axon
    C. dendrites
    D. axon terminals

7. A neuron will fire when a rapid reversal of negative and positive ions stimulate the cell and reach a level of intensity that is above the cell's: (48)
   A. potential.
   B. threshold.
   C. spikes.
   D. resting level.

8. Suppose a researcher has determined that a particular illness is caused by excessive action of a particular neurotransmitter. The researcher will probably try to create a drug that will act as a(n)_____ for that neurotransmitter. (51)
   A. agonist
   B. antagonist
   C. neuropeptide
   D. synapse

9. Endorphins: (50)
   A. are narcotic drugs.
   B. excite synaptic transmission of pain.
   C. inhibit synaptic transmission of pain.
   D. are incomplete amino acids and ineffective as neurotransmitters.

10. The parasympathetic nervous system is primarily responsible for (53)
    A. helping relax and conserve energy
    B. coping with emergency situations
    C. muscular coordination and movements
    D. processing sensory inputs to the brain

11. Your body assumes a "fight-or-flight" condition, preparing you for emergency situations, when the _____ nervous system is activated. (53)
    A. central
    B. somatic
    C. sympathetic
    D. parasympathetic

12. The basal ganglia are nuclei that are important for controlling (58)
    A. communication between the hemispheres
    B. movement and posture
    C. sleepiness and alertness
    D. strong emotions such as anger and fear.

13. Which of the following is not a spinal reflex? (54)
    A. knee jerk
    B. removing your hand from a hot object
    C. reaching for a candy bar
    D. pulling your foot from the cold water in a swimming pool

14. The technique for measuring neuronal activity that involves placing a microelectrode next to a neuron is called: (58-59)
    A.    electroencephalography.
    B.    magnetic resonance imaging.
    C.    computerized axial tomography.
    D.    single unit recording.

15. The limbic system: (57)
    A.    is probably one of the most complex and least understood areas of the brain.
    B.    is involved in memory, emotional behavior, and epilepsy.
    C.    contains "pleasure centers."
    D.    all of the above

16. The reticular formation that extends through the hindbrain, the midbrain, and forebrain is thought to be involved in: (55)
    A.    coordination of smooth muscle.
    B.    experiencing pain.
    C.    controlling heart beat.
    D.    waking and sleeping.

17. Plasticity, or malleability, refers to the brain's ability to (64)
    A.    fill the entire space of the skull with structures.
    B.    communicate between the two brain hemispheres.
    C.    change its functioning as a result of experience.
    D.    predict how it should be organized.

18. Hypoglycemia is a condition caused by: (66)
    A.    too much thyroxin.
    B.    too little thyroxin.
    C.    too little insulin.
    D.    too much insulin.

19. When looking at gender differences, we find that: (63-64)
    A.    hormones have no effect on behavior.
    B.    there are greater differences among women and among men than between women and men.
    C.    testosterone is a hormone found only in men.
    D.    structural differences in the brain are apparent at birth.

20. What are the basic building blocks of the nervous system called? (46)
    A.    synapses
    B.    nerves
    C.    grey cells
    D.    neurons

21. Name the part of the neuron that carries information toward the cell body. (47)
    A.  dendrites
    B.  synapse
    C.  axon
    D.  myelin

22. How can the electrochemical process that produces an action potential be best described? (48)
    A.  a chemical change that occurs as a result of electrical stimulation
    B.  an exchange of ions through the cell membrane
    C.  a molecular chain reaction
    D.  the creation of chemical transmitters by electrical energy

23. Select the neurotransmitter that is especially involved with anxiety. (50)
    A.  GABA
    B.  acetylcholine
    C.  serotonin
    D.  norepinephrine

24. What are the two divisions of the peripheral nervous system called? (52)
    A.  endogenous and exogenous systems
    B.  sympathetic and parasympathetic systems
    C.  somatic and autonomic systems
    D.  sensory and motor systems

25. An individual with an impaired somatic nervous system may have difficulty with which of the following activities? (52)
    A.  mentally adding two numbers together
    B.  digesting food
    C.  spading a garden
    D.  daydreaming

26. Which of the following is likely to be disrupted in an individual with a damaged cerebellum? (55)
    A.  sleeping
    B.  playing basketball
    C.  thinking
    D.  homeostasis

27. For what reason might an individual have his/her corpus callosum surgically severed? (62)
    A.  to limit the severity of epileptic seizures
    B.  to treat severe depression and other mental illness
    C.  to control outbursts of rage and anger
    D.  to provide subjects for split-brain research

28. Which of the following are prominent areas of study focusing upon the influence of nature on an individual? (38-41)
    A. genetics
    B. twin studies
    C. heredity
    D. all of the above

29. _____ neurons carry information from the central nervous system to the glands and muscles. (46)
    A. Inter
    B. Sensory
    C. Motor
    D. Afferent

30. The _____ nervous system comprises part of the peripheral nervous system and transmits sensory information through both afferent and efferent neurons. (52)
    A. Somatic
    B. Autonomic
    C. Sympathetic
    D. Parasympathetic

31. The _____ includes brain areas such as the cortex, a thought oriented structure, and the thalamus, which routes information to different parts of the brain. (56-57)
    A. Corpus Callosum
    B. Hindbrain
    C. Midbrain
    D. Forebrain

32. _____ is a brain monitoring technique that tracks the regional blood flow during various mental tasks using radioactive markers. (59-60)
    A. Magnetic Resonance Imaging
    B. Computerized Tomography
    C. Positron Emission Tomography
    D. Electroencephalography

33. Which of the following is not knowledge garnered through split-brain patient studies? (61-63)
    A. Not every behavior or function is associated with a single part of the brain.
    B. Severing of the Corpus Callosum produces ambidextrous abilities
    C. Specific localization of certain functions
    D. Performance on certain tasks is decremented due to the inability of the left and right hemispheres to communicate

34. The central nervous system effects the release of _____ which then impact _____ to ultimately impact human behavior. (65-66)
    A.   glands, organs
    B.   organs, hormones
    C.   hormones, glands
    D.   hormones, organs

35. The _____ is directly related to the development of disorders involving the over or underproduction of insulin. (66)
    A.   Pituitary Gland
    B.   Pancreas
    C.   Adrenal Gland
    D.   Salivary Gland

36. The _____ is the small space that separates the signal transmission center from one neuron and the receptor centers of another neuron. (48)
    A.   axon
    B.   dendrite
    C.   synapse
    D.   action potential

37. How is it possible to have two people in which the genetic heritage is the same but the environment is not? (41)
    A.   Paternal twins, reared apart
    B.   Identical twins, reared apart
    C.   Monoclonal twins, reared apart
    D.   Nothing; this is NOT possible

38. The long slim fiber that extends from a neuron and that carries its message out to other neurons is called the (47)
    A.   dendrite.
    B.   glia.
    C.   myelin.
    D.   axon.

39. When a postsynaptic potential (PSP) is received by a cell, if it is excitatory it will _____ while if it is inhibitory it will _____. (49-50)
    A.   trigger then release of neurotransmitters; trigger the absorption of neurotransmitters.
    B.   trigger the absorption of neurotransmitters; trigger the release of neurotransmitters.
    C.   make the cell fire more easily; make the cell fire less easily.
    D.   make the cell fire less easily; make the cell fire more easily.

40. The peripheral nervous system consists of two parts, which are (51-52)
    A. the brain and the spinal cord.
    B. the parasympathetic and sympathetic nervous systems.
    C. the somatic and the autonomic nervous systems.
    D. the afferent and the efferent fibers.

41. The sympathetic nervous system is primarily responsible for (53)
    A. helping relax and conserve energy.
    B. processing sensory inputs to the brain.
    C. muscular coordination and movements.
    D. coping with emergency situations.

42. Which of the following parts of the brain is most heavily involved in regulating emotions? (57-58)
    A. The cerebellum
    B. The reticular formation
    C. The limbic system
    D. The corpus callosum

43. A CT scan (computerized tomography) is created using (59)
    A. electrodes attached to the outside of someone's head.
    B. Computer controlled and processed X-ray pictures.
    C. radiochemicals injected into the patient's blood.
    D. the magnetic fields of varying strength and direction.

44. The relationships between the endocrine glands, the brain, and behavior can best be summarized by saying (65-66)
    A. the endocrine glands control the brain through the hormones they secrete into the bloodstream.
    B. the brain controls the endocrine glands and the hormones they produce through nerve signals.
    C. Hormones produced by the endocrine glands affect behavior through their effect on the brain.
    D. The endocrine glands, the brain, and behavior all interact and affect each other.

45. One way in which men and women use their brains differently when performing the same task is that (63-64)
    A. men process language primarily on the right side, women primarily on the left.
    B. men's brains process more tasks at lower levels, women more at higher levels.
    C. men's brains are less affected by hormones than women's brains are.
    D. women use both sides of their brains more equally on some cognitive tasks.

# When You Have Finished

## Essay Questions

1. Describe the action potential of the neuron. (48)

2. What is the human genome and why is mapping it important? (40-41)

3. What is psychopharmacology and where is the focus of much of its research? (50-51)

4. Define behavioral determinism and the evidence against it. (45)

5. Describe the interaction between the sympathetic and somatic nervous system during the fight-or-flight state  (53)

# Chapter 3

# Child Development

## Before you read...

In this chapter we return to the question of nature versus nurture by looking at child development. Twin studies provide interesting and intriguing information about the contributions of genetics and the environment. Three theoretical orientations that are considered by developmental psychologists are the psychoanalytic approach, behaviorism and cognitive theory. Researchers use two methods to study child development. In cross-sectional research many individuals at a variety of ages are investigated simultaneously. In longitudinal research the same individuals are followed over a period of time. Each provides valuable information.

The prenatal period is the first developmental stage and extends from conception to birth. During this critical period, development may be affected by environmental variables. Factors such as diet, infection, radiation, and drugs have the potential to affect the mother and the child. Substances known as teratogens can cause birth defects and may lead to early infant death. Many substances like alcohol, cigarettes, certain foods, and drugs can have teratogenic effects. Therefore, both parents should take cautions to avoid any potential harm. The prenatal period ends with the birth process.

The period of infancy (birth to 18 months) is a time of dramatic growth and change. Newborns can hear, see, smell, and respond to the environment immediately after leaving the birth canal. Newborns exhibit several reflexive behaviors at birth which are indicative of sound neurological development and, in just a few short months, develop complex perceptual skills such as pattern recognition and depth perception.

The physical development of children is dramatic and exciting. Cognitive development is equally dramatic and exhilarating. In the first two years of life a child learns to assimilate and accommodate information into a developmental process that lasts, for a lifetime. Piaget describes child development in four stages. The *sensorimotor* stage (birth ≈ 2 years) is considered by Piaget to be the most significant. In just two years the child develops from a reflexive organism into a fully responsive individual, exhibiting independence of movement and early language. The *preoperational* stage (from 2 ≈ 7) is the time when a child begins to be less self-centered through a process called decentration. The third stage of *concrete* operations (from 6 or 7 ≈ 11 or 12) is highlighted by the development of conservation skills. The final stage of Piaget's cognitive development is called formal operations (age 12 and beyond). In this stage, children begin to engage in abstract thought processes and eventually develop into adults. Piaget has had a tremendous effect on the way we look at early child development. He has influenced many of the methods used by educators and parents alike. However, his theory is a stage theory and many critics argue that his stages are not universal. Vygotsky's view is that children may not have the innate ability to develop complex cognitive skills without the help of their society (usually parents). You should use your critical thinking skills to form your own opinions.

Children also develop a sense of morality primarily from their parents, teachers, and society. Children will begin with a black-and-white view of morality and develop into more complex situational views as described by Kohlberg's stages of moral development. Kohlberg outlines three stages of moral development, including preconventional, conventional, and postconventional levels.

Attachment and bonding are examined by Lefton as components of a child's emotional development. He also describes how verbal exchanges between children and their caregivers help them learn socialization skills. One emotion that appears to be longlasting is temperament. Research indicates that there are four broad categories of temperament: easy, difficult, slow-to-warm-up, and unique.

This chapter concludes with a discussion of some very important issues in the social development of a child. The child's early interactive learning plays an important role in a developing personality. Parents have great influence in determining the child's gender-based interests. Erikson's psychosocial stage theory is presented in part to show how the child searches for self-identity.

# Chapter Objectives

- Understand the issues in developmental psychology
- Know the strengths and weaknesses of cross-sectional and longitudinal research designs
- Describe prenatal development and what may impact development.
- Define critical periods
- Understand infant perceptions
- Describe Piaget's theory and stages
- Describe Vygotsky's theory
- Understand Theory of Mind
- Know Kohlberg's levels and stages of moral development
- Define attachment and infant attachment styles
- Define temperament and its categories
- Describe early social development
- Understand gender roles and gender stereotypes
- Know Erikson's first 4 stages of psychsocial development

# As you read...

## Key Issues and Research Designs

1. Define Developmental Psychology.

2. What is the goal of Developmental psychologists?

| 3-1 | Issues in Developmental Psychology |
|-----|-----|

3. What are the 3 main issues of developmental psychology?

4. Revisit the nature/nurture controversy in the context of human development.

5. How do the Evolutionary psychologists explain individual differences in development?

| 3-2 | Developmental Theories |
|-----|-----|

6. Compare the different theoretical perspectives of human development.

7. According to _____, human development is based on a system of reinforcement and consequences.

| 3-3 | Research Designs |
|-----|-----|

8. Define Cross-Sectional and Longitudinal research designs.

9. Psychologist use _____ _____ to study individuals over time and _____ _____ research to look at individuals of different ages at the same time.

# Physical Development

1. What are prenatal events?

2. What are neonatal events?

| 3-4 | **Prenatal Development** |
|---|---|

3. Describe human development during the prenatal stage of life.

4. Define Zygote, Embryo, and Fetus.

5. The mass of tissue that provides oxygen, food, and antibodies to the fetus and eliminates waste is called the _____.

6. The _____ connects the zygote to the placenta.

| 3-5 | **Harmful Environment Effects** |
|---|---|

7. Describe environmental factors that affect prenatal development.

8. Define and discuss the damage teratogens can cause during fetal development.

| 3-6 | **Newborns Come Well-Equipped** |
|---|---|

9. List and describe the 5 primary reflexes of a newborn.

10. For what time period is the child considered to be in infancy?

11. Describe the 2 growth patterns.

12.	The _____ reflex is an outstretching of the arms and legs and crying in response to a loud noise.

13.	When one touches the sole of the foot of an infant, which causes the toes to turn upward and out, the _____ reflex is exhibited.

14.	Describe the Fantz's viewing box and how it is used to study infant perception

15	List some of the visual preferences of infants.

16.	Define Critical Periods.

17.	The _____ _____ _____ was established to test the depth perception of an infant.

# The Development of Thought

| 3-7 | Jean Piaget's Insights |
|---|---|

1.	Define Schema.

2.	What are the three processes by which a schema can change?

3.	Define assimilation and accommodation.

4.	List Piaget's four stages of intellectual development, the age range that each state encompasses, and the major intellectual accomplishment associated with each stage

| | Stage | Age | Major Accomplishment |
|---|---|---|---|
| 1. | _____ | _____ | _____ |
| 2. | _____ | _____ | _____ |
| 3. | _____ | _____ | _____ |
| 4. | _____ | _____ | _____ |

5. The realization that objects continue to exist even when they are out of sight is called
   _____ _____.

6. The inability to perceive a situation except in relation to oneself is called
   _____.

7. _____ is the process after Piaget's preoperational stage in which children
   differentiate between feelings, ideas, and interests.

8. _____ is the ability to see that objects may be transformed, yet may
   still be the same amount of weight, substance, or volume.

9. Define Ecological Systems Theory.

| 3-8 | Vygotsky's Sociocultural Theory: An Alternative to Piaget |
|---|---|

10. What are the differences between Vygotsky's and Piaget's approaches?

11. Define what Vygotsky means by scaffolding and how it applies to the learning
    processs.

12.    Define Theory of Mind.

13.    What type of research is used to study Theory of Mind?

3-10    **Thought in a Social Context**

14.    Describe Project Head Start.

15.    What makes an intervention more effective?

3-11    **Moral Reasoning**

16.    Define morality.

17.    Define moral relativity.

18.    Compare and contrast Piaget's and Kohlberg's theories of moral development.

19.    List the 3 levels with their 2 stages of Kohlberg's theory of moral development.

20.    What is the distinction between sex and gender?

21.    _____ _____ are differences between mean and women on behaviors or mental processes.

## The Growth of Emotions

3-12    **Attachment: The Ties that Bind**

1.  Define Attachment.

2.  Define Bonding.

3.  _____ _____ is a fear response when an attachment figure leaves an infant.

4.  Describe the 3 attachment types demonstrated by the strange situation technique.

5.  What does the research show about the effects of leaving children in the care of someone other than their parents?

6.  What is the evolutionary perspective on attachment?

7.  What cues do children read?

| 3-13 | Temperament |
|------|-------------|

8.  Define Temperament.

9.  List the 4 broad categories of temperament.

10. Can temperament be changed?

11. Is Ritalin misused?

## Social Development

| 3-14 | Early Social Development and Child Rearing |
|------|--------------------------------------------|

1.  Describe the social interactions of the child during its first two years of life.

2.  Describe Black, Dubowitz and Starr's study of fathers' interactions.

## 3-15    Gender Roles

3.    The behavior patterns that are expected because of one's gender are known as

_____    _____.

4.    What must researchers look at to accurately analyze gender differences.

5.    Define Gender Stereotypes.

6.    Why does gender separation occur?

## 3-16    Erik Erikson and the Beginning of the Search for Self

7.    Describe the first 4 stages of Erikson's psychosocial development.

8.    At what age does each stage occur?

**Term Identification: Make flashcards for each of the following terms. Hint: Use the definitions in the margins of the chapter**

Developmental Psychology
Zygote
Embryo
Fetus
Placenta
Teratogen
Babinski Reflex
Moro Reflex
Rooting Reflex
Sucking Reflex
Grasping Reflex
Critical Period
Scheme
Assimilation
Accomodation
Sensorimotor Stage

Preoperational Stage
Egocentrism
Decentration
Concrete Operational Stage
Conservation
Formal Operational Stage
Theory of Mind
Morality
Sex
Gender
Attachment
Bonding
Temperament
Gender Stereotype
Androgynous

# After you read . . . Self Test

## Chapter 3 Self Test

1. The disadvantages of longitudinal studies are: (75)
   A. subjects' backgrounds differ.
   B. subjects may move, withdraw, or even die.
   C. behavior or performance of a task or ability may reflect their subjects' predisposition, i.e., liking of the task.
   D. individual differences are impossible to assess.

2. An individual's basic characteristics, such as eye color and sex, are determined _____ fertilization. (76)
   A. prior to
   B. within minutes after
   C. about ten hours after
   D. four to eight weeks after

3. Dr. Grau believes that development is a process of change that occurs at various critical periods and changes appear abruptly. Dr. Grau then, believes that development is a _____ process. (73)
   A. stable
   B. volatile
   C. continuous
   D. discontinuous

4. Environmental factors such as _____ affect both the mother and the fetus. (76)
   A. diet, infection, radiation, drugs
   B. diet, infection, drugs
   C. diet, infection, radiation
   D. diet, drugs, radiation

5. A developmental theorist, who believes that early childhood experiences shape a person's biologically based urges, subscribes to the _____ perspective. (74)
   A. behaviorist
   B. psychoanalytic
   C. cognitive
   D. ecological systems

6. _____ are substances that can cause developmental malformations. (77)
   A. Schemas
   B. Malformers
   C. Teratogens
   D. Placenta

7.  Newborn babies prefer to stare at (80)
    A.  random patterns.
    B.  simple patterns.
    C.  human faces.
    D.  breasts.

8.  If an infant's lips or cheeks are touched, it will turn its head toward the stimulus because of the _____ reflex. (79)
    A.  sucking
    B.  rooting
    C.  Babinski
    D.  Moro

9.  Infancy is defined as ending and childhood as beginning when the child (78)
    A.  is 18-24 months old
    B.  can stand without support.
    C.  begins to use language to describe experiences.
    D.  drops the rooting reflex and uses learned behaviors in its place.

10. The visual cliff is applied to a baby to measure the (81)
    A.  primary reflexes.
    B.  visual preferences.
    C.  depth perception.
    D.  cognitive development

11. According to Piaget, during which developmental stage do children begin to learn to manipulate the environment? (85)
    A.  the preoperational stage
    B.  the sensorimotor stage
    C.  the formal operational stage
    D.  the concrete operational stage

12. The major difference between children in the concrete operational stage and the preoperational stage of development is that in the concrete operational stage children (86)
    A.  understand the concept of conservation.
    B.  develop a sense of object permanence.
    C.  are generally more egocentric.
    D.  can think logically about hypothetical things.

13. Urie Bronfenbrenner is most closely associated with which developmental theory. (89)
    A.  psychoanalytic.
    B.  behaviorist.
    C.  cognitive.
    D.  ecological systems.

14. Assimilation and accommodation occur in which stages of Piaget's theory of development? (84)
    A.  1 and 2
    B.  2 and 3
    C.  3 and 4
    D.  A and C

15. The preoperational stage occurs from (86)
    A.  birth to age two.
    B.  age seven to age eleven.
    C.  age two to age six.
    D.  age eleven.

16. Decentration is (86)
    A.  the ability to recognize that objects may be transformed visually or physically, yet represent the same amount of weight or volume.
    B.  the ability to understand the difference between their interests and those of others.
    C.  the belief that the world exists solely to satisfy the needs and interests of the child.
    D.  the ability to recognize that objects continue to exist even when they are out of sight.

17. Piaget's theory focuses on (84)
    A.  thought processes.
    B.  content.
    C.  intellectual development.
    D.  social development.

18. Vance and his mother bought a puzzle at the store. The puzzle was harder than any Vance had previously worked. Vance's mother sat on the floor with him and gave instructions when Vance could not make any more progress on his own. According to Vygotsky, Vance's mother was: (90)
    A.  interfering with Vance's learning.
    B.  not giving Vance enough observational help.
    C.  being overly intrusive to the learning process.
    D.  scaffolding Vance's skills.

19. Charles believes it is acceptable for a starving man to steal food because even though stealing is against the law, a man must do whatever it takes to survive. At what level of moral reasoning is Charles? (93)
    A.  preconventional
    B.  postconventional
    C.  conventional
    D.  relative

20. Gilligan's work dealing with gender differences in moral reasoning suggests that (94)
    A.  boys gravitate more toward morality of domination.
    B.  boys gravitate more toward morality of caring.
    C.  girls gravitate more toward morality of justice.
    D.  girks gravitate more toward morality of caring.

21. Some researchers claim that Piaget may have overestimated the extent of
    _____ in young children. (89)
    A.   egocentrism
    B.   maturity
    C.   cognitive development
    D.   age

22. According to Bowlby, a baby's interactions with parents during the first few months of
    life (96)
    A.   are primarily focused on food and safety.
    B.   are more meaningful for the parents than the baby.
    C.   are crucial to survival and normal development.
    D.   will be replaced by stronger feelings at the end of the year.

23. Long –lasting differences in the intensity and quality of a person's emotional reactions is
    referred to as (99)
    A.   conditioning.
    B.   attachment.
    C.   egocentrism.
    D.   temperament.

24. Six-month-old Sydney is a baby who does well on a set routine. However, when Sydney
    and her parents went out of town on vacation Sydney did not react well and appeared
    "out of sorts" the entire time. Which category best describes Sydney's temperamental
    style? (99)
    A.   slow-to-warm-up
    B.   difficult
    C.   easy
    D.   unique

25. The social development of infants is the first year of life is largely focused on (103)
    A.   developing a sense of self
    B.   forming relationships with other children
    C.   the infant's own needs
    D.   learning to share and take turns

26. Carol Gilligan found that people use _____ when reasoning moral conflicts. (93-
    94)
    A.   justice
    B.   caring, relationships, and connections with other people
    C.   justice, caring and responsibility, relationships with other people
    D.   justice, caring, relationships, and connections to other people

27. Erikson believed that children are faced with which psychological crisis during their first
    year of life? (106)
    A.   initiative versus guilt
    B.   trust versus mistrust
    C.   industry versus inferiority
    D.   autonomy versus shame/doubt

28. To assess the roles played by genetics and environment, researchers most often study (72)
   A. animal models
   B. identical twins.
   C. parents and their children
   D. college students

29. A developmental theorist who believes that development occurs in a biologically determined sequence and development is a process of adaptation to the world, subscribes to the _____ perspective. (74)
   A. psychoanalytic
   B. behaviorist
   C. ecological systems
   D. cognitive

30. The basic function of the placenta is to (76)
   A. cushion the baby against damage
   B. serve as the baby's life support system
   C. provide stimulation to the prenatal environment
   D. protect the mother from the baby's system

31. What branch of psychology focuses on change in an individual's lifetime? (72)
   A. social
   B. developmental
   C. motivational
   D. personality

32. Which of the following situations will cause the Moro reflex to occur in newborn infants? (79)
   A. a touch on the cheek
   B. pressure on the kneecap
   C. a touch on the bottom of the foot
   D. a sudden change in environmental stimulation

33. What did Frantz use his "viewing box" to study? (80)
   A. the visual preferences of infants
   B. recognition memory in infants
   C. stimulus generalization in infants
   D. the depth perception of infants

34. What was the focus of Piaget's research and theory? (82-84)
   A. individual differences
   B. the content of the mind
   C. thought processes
   D. motivation

35. A child who begins to engage in make-believe play is in which of Piaget's cognitive stages? (86)
    A.   sensorimotor
    B.   concrete operational
    C.   formal operational
    D.   preoperational

36. In which of Piaget's cognitive stages would an individual develop the ability to engage in abstract reasoning and hypothetical events that are not directly experienced? (87)
    A.   concrete operations
    B.   preoperational
    C.   formal operations
    D.   sensorimotor

37. What is the focus of Lawrence Kohlberg's moral development theory? (93)
    A.   the morality of young children
    B.   the morality of adults
    C.   moral behavior
    D.   moral reasoning

38. Which of the following is the central concept in Kohlberg's theory of morality. (93)
    A.   justice
    B.   property rights
    C.   truth
    D.   reciprocity

39. A researcher tests a group of the same children at ages 2, 4, and 6. What experimental design is being used? (74-75)
    A.   cross-sectional
    B.   longitudinal
    C.   tri-sectional
    D.   continuous

40. Before a fertilized egg implants into the uterine wall, it is called a (76)
    A.   zygote
    B.   embryo
    C.   fetus
    D.   neonate

41. When a child learns that a toy continues to exist when it is out of sight, that child has mastered (85)
    A.   conservation
    B.   ego centrism
    C.   decentration
    D.   object permanence

53

42. The only reason Leo does not take a hot cookie off the plate is because his mother would yell at him. Leo is operating at which level of morality? (93)
    A.   pre conventional
    B.   post conventional
    C.   mid conventional
    D.   conventional

43. Most babies have a _____ attachment; they become distressed when their mother leaves, but they are easily comforted. (96)
    A.   avoidant
    B.   resistant
    C.   secure
    D.   disoriented

44. At which of Erikson's stages is toilet training and master of skills important? (106)
    A.   initiative vs. guilt
    B.   autonomy vs. shame and doubt
    C.   trust vs. mistrust
    D.   industry vs. inferiority

45. Meghan knows her daddy's real name is John and she is introduced to a family friend who is also named John. When introduced she says, "your name isn't John that's my daddy's name." According to Piaget, Meghan's error is an example of (84)
    A.   role confusion
    B.   conservation
    C.   assimilation
    D.   accommodation

# When You Have Finished

## Essay Questions

1. Compare and Contrast the strengths and weaknesses of Cross-Sectional and Longitudinal research designs. (74-75)

2. Compare and contrast assimilation and accommodation and describe how they become a learning cycle. (84)

3. A chronically battered wife killed her husband. Discuss how a child at each level of Kohlberg's moral reasoning would respond. (92-93)

4. What is Theory of Mind, when and how does it develop? (90-91)

5. What factors impact father involvement in child rearing? (102-103)

# Chapter 4

# Adolescence and Adulthood

# Before you read...

This chapter discusses the developmental changes that occur following childhood through adulthood. The discussion begins with adolescence, the period between childhood and adulthood. Adolescence is a concept used to describe the transitional period from child to adult. *Psychology* cautions that we must first consider the social and cultural context from which the adolescent develops and that the research findings may not be universal. Adolescence is marked by the significant physical and cognitive changes associated with puberty and the social implications for the adolescent. Adolescents' self-images are influenced by early childhood experiences as well as by involvement in sports, parents, and peers. Additionally, a person's gender identity and sex roles develop during adolescence. Sexual behavior among American adolescents is changing. Parental discipline, relaxed attitudes, and other trends affecting adolescents' sexual behavior are discussed.

An adult's physical change is less dramatic than that of the earlier stages of childhood and adolescence. However, the changes that occur are just as significant. Adult physical fitness, sensory changes, sexual drives, and cognitive processes all go through the aging process. Theories are offered to explain these transitions. Personality seems to be one of the most stable components of development. Erikson's views of adult development are presented. Each stage presents a crisis and each crisis may be resolved in a positive or negative fashion. Levinson offers a differing view of adult development. He suggests that as people grow older they adapt; that four eras present adults with different life structures specific to the individual, and therefore that adaptation is also unique. As all theories are challenged, so is Levinson's. Some contend that he needs to consider more seriously the gender differences in adult development.

There are numerous myths and stereotypes about older people. Lefton and Brannon discuss the realities of this final developmental stage.

# Chapter Objectives

- Understand adolescence and discuss why it must be considered in multiple contexts.
- Describe the physical development that occurs during adolescence and how it can affect the self-image of an adolescent.
- Understand the ways adolescents develop their new cognitive abilities.
- Evaluate the influences on the development of an adolescent's self-esteem and self-identity.
- Understand the significance of friendships in adolescence.
- Understand the factors that contribute to the development of gender identity and gender roles and explain what is meant by androgyny.
- Discuss adolescent sexual behavior.
- Understand how attitudes about sexuality influence social development and personal behavior.
- Outline the physiological, sexual, and sensory changes that occur during adulthood.
- Describe the various theories of aging.
- Describe the cognitive changes that take place during adulthood.
- Understand Erikson's and Levinson's theories of adulthood.
- Discuss how myths and stereotypes have led to a bias against the elderly
- Describe the symptoms of specific brain disorders such as dementia.
- Understand Alzheimer's disease.

# As you read...

## Adolescence: Bridging the Gap

1.  Define Adolescence.

2.  Define Puberty.

3.  A person's actual age in years is known as their _____ _____.

4.  The way a person actually performs is known as their _____ _____.

| 4-1 | We Must View Adolescence in Multiple Contexts |
|---|---|

5.  Does Storm and Stress accurately describe all adolescence?

6.  Why must adolescence be viewed in cultural context?

| 4-2 | Physical Development in Adolescence |
|---|---|

7.  Define growth spurts.

8.  List the male and female secondary sex characteristics.

9.  Are there advantages for the early-maturing adolescent?

| 4-3 | Cognitive Development in Adolescence |
|---|---|

10.  What are the two cognitive distortions of adolescence?

11.  Are there ethnic differences in cognitive development?

12.   Should adolescents be able to make their own medical decisions?

---

**4-4      Emotional and Social Development in Adolescence**

13.   What are 3 important sources of influence on the self-esteem and personality of adolescents?

14.   A _____ _____, which can be influential, is a group of people that identify with and compare themselves to each other.

15.   What impact does the sex of siblings have on gender roles?

---

**4-5      Who Am I? The Search for Gender Identity**

16.   Define Gender Identity.

17.   _____ _____ is the exaggeration of traditional male or female behaviors.

18.   Describe Gender Schema Theory.

19.   A conceptual framework that organizes information so that one can make sense of the world is a _____.

20.   Define androgyny.

21.   Define Anorexia Nervosa.

22.   Define Bulimia Nervosa.

---

**4-6      Real Men and Women**

23.   What is a gendered society?

24.     What is the challenge for parents, educators and psychologists to end gender stereotyping?

4-7     Who Are My Friends?

25.     Define friendship.

26.     How do adult friendships between woman differ from friendships between men.

27.     What is the evolutionary approach to friends then lovers?

4-8     Sexual Behavior During Adolescence

28.     What changes in adolescent sexual behavior have occurred?

29.     What are the consequences of these changes?

30.     Each year over _____ unmarried teenage girls become pregnant in the United States

# Adulthood: Years of Stability and Change

1.     What does Wallerstein's research indicate about the effects of divorce on children?

2.     Are her predictions the same for all families?

4-9     Physical Changes

3.     Define fitness.

4. What fitness changes occur in adulthood?

5. _____ is a condition in which bone mass and strength decreases.

6. What sensory changes occur in adulthood?

7. Many people can no longer hear _____-_____ sounds by age 65.

8. Define menopause?

9. What sexual changes occur in men in adulthood?

10. What are the 3 basic types of aging theories?

11. _____ is the process by which cells kill themselves.

12. What are telomers?

13. Describe the wear-and tear theory of aging.

14. The _____ theory of aging states that the body's ability to adjust to stress and variations in internal conditions decreases with age.

15. Compare primary aging and secondary aging.

| 4-10 | **Cognitive Changes** |
|------|------------------------|

16. What cognitive changes occur after age 60?

17. Drastic declines in _____ _____ with age are not universal.

18.     What social changes does middle aged adult face?

19.     What social changes are the focus for older adults?

20.     Complete the table below.

**Erikson's Psychosocial Stage Theory**

| Stage | Age | Events | Description of Conflict |
|---|---|---|---|
| Identity vs. Role Confusion | Adolescence | | |
| Intimacy vs. Isolation | Young Adulthood | | |
| Generativity vs. Stagnation | Middle Adulthood | | |
| Ego Integrity vs. Despair | Late Adulthood | | |

21.     Describe the 4 eras outlined by Levinson, including the ages for each.

22.     Define midlife transition.

23.     How are the life stages different for women?

4-12    **Personality Development**

24.     What is the basic tenet of personality theories?

25.     Why have women undergone special scrutiny in personality research since the 1970's?

# Late Adulthood: Growing Older, Growing Wiser

| 4-13 | Myths, Reality and Stereotypes |
|------|-------------------------------|

1.   Define Ageism.

2.   Complete the following table

| Age | Physical Change | Cognitive Change | Work Roles | Personal Development | Major Tasks |
|-----|----------------|------------------|------------|---------------------|-------------|
| Middle Adulthood 40-65 | | | | | |
| Late Adulthood 65-75+ | | | | | |

| 4-14 | Health in Late Adulthood |
|------|--------------------------|

3.   Define dementia.

4.   Define the 3 main types of dementia.

5.   _____% of the people between the ages of 75-59 suffer from dementia.

6.   Define Alzheimer's disease and its symptoms.

7.    What is terminal drop.


8.    Define thanatology.

**Term Identification: Make flashcards for each of the following terms.
Hint: Use the definitions in the margins of the chapter**

Adolescence
Puberty
Secondary Sex Characteristics
Imaginary Audience
Personal Fable
Gender Identity
Gender Schema Theory
Gender Role
Gender Role Stereotype

Androgynous
Eating Disorders
Anorexia Nervosa
Bulimia Nervosa
Ageism
Dementia
Alzheimer's Disease
Thanatology

# After you read . . . Self Test

## Chapter 4 Self Test

1. _____ is the period of human development that bridges childhood and adulthood. (112)
   A.   Puberty
   B.   Menarche
   C.   Idiosyncrasy
   D.   Adolescence

2. Most research on adolescence has been conducted on: (113)
   A.   white teenagers.
   B.   black teenagers.
   C.   middle class teenagers.
   D.   Both A and C

3. Just before the onset of puberty, boys and girls experience significant growth spurts, gaining as much as _____ inches in a year. (114)
   A.   four
   B.   five
   C.   six
   D.   three

4. Facial hair, chest hair, and breasts are all examples of _____. (114)
   A.   gonadotrophs.
   B.   primary sex characteristics
   C.   secondary sex characteristics
   D.   pubertal markers

5. Peer groups consist of people of the same (120)
   A.   age.
   B.   sex.
   C.   race.
   D.   all of the above

6. Gender schema (121)
   A.   is a person's sense of being male or female.
   B.   is a social category.
   C.   asserts children use gender as an organizing theme to help them understand their world perceptions.
   D.   states that the way a person is raised and taught has a profound impact on behavior and seems to have a gender related component.

7. Behaviors that are shared by both sexes are: (123)
   A.   gender based.
   B.   androgynous.
   C.   role based.
   D.   stereotypical.

8. Which of the following ethnic groups most fear the consequences of a poor education (116)
   A.   Hispanic-American
   B.   White-American
   C.   African-American
   D.   Asian-American

9. A person's sense of being either male or female is their_____. (121)
   A.   gender identity
   B.   gender schema
   C.   gender role
   D.   gender stereotype

10. Identity versus role confusion is the _____ stage of Erikson's theory. (131)
    A.   fifth
    B.   fourth
    C.   seventh
    D.   sixth

11. In the last few decades, what change has occurred in adolescent sexual behavior? (125)
    A.   Teens are acting the same but talking about it more
    B.   Teens are having sex at earlier ages than before
    C.   Only teens from minority groups are having sex earlier
    D.   There has been no change in sexual behavior at all

12. According to your text, more than _____ unmarried adolescent girls in the United States get pregnant each year. (126)
    A.   250,000
    B.   500,000
    C.   750,000
    D.   1,000,000

13. Physically, human beings are at their peak of agility, speed, and strength between ages (127)
    A.   11-17.
    B.   20-30.
    C.   18-30.
    D.   18-25.

14. By age _____, most people can no longer hear high-frequency sounds. (128)
    A.   50
    B.   60
    C.   65
    D.   70

15. New dilemmas, challenges, and responsibilities that require reassessment, reappraisal, and development of new skills are (132)
    A. transitions.
    B. mid-life crisis.
    C. transition-crisis.
    D. none of the above

16. Menopause occurs when women are approximately _____ years old and results is _____. (128-129)
    A. 50;loss of sexual desire
    B. 50;cessation of ovulation and menstruation
    C. 40; loss of sexual desire.
    D. 40;cessation of ovulation and menstruation.

17. The three basic types of theories of aging emphasize (129)
    A. diet, exercise and stress.
    B. heredity, external factors, and physiology.
    C. lifestyle, the physical environment, and attitudes toward life.
    D. medical care, social integration, and personality.

18. The theory of aging that emphasizes loss of the ability of the body to adjust to changing conditions is called the _____ theory (130)
    A. homeostatic
    B. adaptation
    C. efficiency
    D. biobehavioral

19. According to Levinson's theory we can think of a person's life as (132)
    A. the development of stable life structures to get them through life.
    B. made up of several stages.
    C. a period during which individuals work out various developmental tasks.
    D. alternating between stable periods and transitional periods.

20. According to Erikson, _____ is a psychological crisis that middle adults face (131)
    A. ego-integrity versus despair
    B. identity versus role confusion
    C. generativity versus stagnation
    D. intimacy versus isolation

21. Which of the following is not one of the traditionally held myths about the elderly? (135)
    A. inflexible.
    B. financially secure.
    C. incompetent.
    D. unhealthy.

22. Ageism is exceptionally prevalent in: (136)
    A.   the media.
    B.   everyday language.
    C.   housing.
    D.   Both A & B

23. Seventy-year-old Thomas views his life as a series of "missed opportunities." He feels that he should have done more with his life. According to Erikson, Thomas has developed a sense of _____ regarding his past. (131)
    A.   confusion
    B.   despair
    C.   isolation
    D.   stagnation

24. Reversible dementias are caused by all but which of the following. (137)
    A.   toxins
    B.   alcoholism
    C.   strokes
    D.   malnutrition

25. Terminal drop is: (138)
    A.   the year before death.
    B.   rapid physical decline.
    C.   rapid intellectual decline.
    D.   Both A & C

26. Mark is seventy-five- years old. He is having severe lapses of memory, judgment, and personality changes, and they are progressively getting worse. It is likely that Mark is suffering from _____. (137)
    A.   ageism
    B.   Parkinson's disease
    C.   psychosis
    D.   dementia

27. _____ is a chronic and progressive disorder of the brain and the most common cause of degenerative dementia in the United States (137)
    A.   Alzheimer's disease
    B.   Parkinson's disease
    C.   Osteoporosis
    D.   Neurofibromatosis

28. Puberty is defined by (112)
    A.   psychological changes
    B.   physiological changes
    C.   cultural standards
    D.   behavioral symptoms

29. When discussing the psychology of adolescence, it is very important to keep in mind that: (113)
   A.   adolescence is invariably a time of severe discord between parents and their adolescent child.
   B.   individuals experience more psychological problems during adolecece than during any other developmental period.
   C.   adolescence, by definition, is invariably a time of storm and stress.
   D.   the majority of youths do not experience major psychological disturbances during the adolescent period.

30. Fourteen-year-old Sara had a zit on her cheek on day. Sarah tried hard to hide her face all day at school. She thought that everyone she came into contact with would be disgusted if they saw her blemish. Sarah's thinking illustrates the adolescent cognitive distortion of_____. (115)
   A.   hypothetical-deductive reasoning
   B.   the imaginary audience
   C.   latent egocentrism
   D.   the personal fable

31. Tommy, a seventeen-year-old male, knew that he probably shouldn't get in the car after having had four beers to drink. However, as he turned on the ignition to the car, he thought to himself, "I won't have a wreck." Tommy's thought process illustrates the adolescent cognitive distortion of _____. (115-116)
   A.   hypothetical-deductive reasoning
   B.   the imaginary audience
   C.   latent egocentrism
   D.   the personal fable

32. Which of the following activities would make one suspect that Susan is an androgynous individual? (123)
   A.   dancing with another girl
   B.   changing the spark plugs in her car
   C.   helping her father clean the kitchen
   D.   helping her mother do the grocery shopping

33. Which of the following concepts was originated by Erik Erikson? (131)
   A.   midlife crisis
   B.   hospice
   C.   identity crisis
   D.   androgyny

34. Which parenting style seems to be associated with high achievement among school students? (116)
   A.   An accepting, tolerant, permissive style
   B.   A stern, uncompromising autocratic style
   C.   A warm, loving, but firm authoritative
   D.   A distant, managerial leadership style

35. Research has shown that negative feelings that arise during puberty can be reduced by involvement in (120)
    A. athletics
    B. hobbies
    C. clubs and organizations
    D. religious groups


36. The exaggeration of traditional male or female behaviors is called (121)
    A. gender identification
    B. gender intensification
    C. gender differentiation
    D. gender pluralization

37. Decreases in bone mass and strength, especially in women after menopause is called (128)
    A. osteogenesis
    B. osteobiflex
    C. osteodisintegration
    D. osteoporosis

38. What is a major problem of being older? (134)
    A. society's negative attitudes toward the elderly
    B. lack of friends
    C. experiential aging
    D. finding useful and interesting things to do

39. It is predicted that John will have a long life because his parents are presently over 85. This prediction is based on the _____ theory of aging. (129)
    A. congenital
    B. heredity
    C. familial
    D. homologous

40. About what percent of adults aged 60 and older report engaging in sexual activity at least once a month? (129)
    A. 20%
    B. 30%
    C. 40%
    D. 50%

41. Which of the following statements is true regarding the sensory changes that occur during adulthood (128)
    A.  Older adults generally have some degree of hearing loss, especially for low frequency sounds
    B.  Older females usually have a higher degree of hearing loss than do their male counterparts
    C.  Dark adaptation is one of the few sensory capabilities that remains constant through out early, middle, and late adulthood
    D.  Older adults need a higher level of stimulation to be able to taste and smell like they did when they were younger

42. The external factors theory of aging emphasizes such things as (129)
    A.  where people live
    B.  whether people smoke
    C.  whether people are overweight
    D.  all of the above

43. The theory of aging that claims that human organisms wear out from overuse is called the _____ theory. (130)
    A.  mechanistic
    B.  wear-and-tear
    C.  homeostatic
    D.  external factors

44. The first era in Levinson's theory is (132)
    A.  infancy and early childhood
    B.  adolescence
    C.  youth
    D.  early adulthood

45. In Erikson's theory of psychosocial development, young adulthood is a time when people struggle with the issue of (131)
    A.  intimacy versus isolation
    B.  generativity versus stagnation
    C.  identity versus confusion
    D.  ego integrity versus despair

# When You Have Finished

## Essay Questions:

1. Compare and Contrast Anorexia and Bulimia (117-118)

2. Describe the imaginary audience and the personal fable and how they affect adolescent behaviors. (115-116)

3. What are the basic differences between Erikson's and Levinson's theories. (131-132)

4. Discuss the developmental consequences of having friends? (124)

5. Describe the cognitive changes after age 65 and why these do not have a large impact on elderly individuals. (130)

# Chapter 5

## Sensation and Perception

# Before you read...

Psychologists study perception primarily because what people sense and perceive determines how they interpret their environment. Psychophysics is the study of how physical stimuli are translated into psychological experience. *Psychology* describes the different types of thresholds thought to be necessary for perception, including a discussion of the possibility of subliminal perception. Although we can multitask some behaviors (walking and chewing gum), we must <u>choose</u> to attend to selected stimuli presented to the auditory and visual systems. Psychologists are interested in how we choose to selectively attend. Sensory restriction is being studied as a means of relaxing, with the possibility that it may be effective in altering such behaviors as smoking and insomnia.

The primary sensory processing system is the visual system. The structure and function of the eye is discussed in detail. Photoreceptors such as rods and cones have implications for visual behavior such as dark adaptation, fine discrimination, and color vision. Researchers are using knowledge about the electrochemical process of stimulation to formulate theories about the visual process, associating receptive fields with body movements and recognition of common objects such as faces.

Your eyes are constantly in motion. Saccades are voluntary eye movements involved in reading, driving, and looking for objects. Color vision has three psychological properties-hue, brightness, and saturation-which correspond to the physical properties of wavelength, intensity, and purity. The trichromatic and opponent-process theories attempt to explain how we perceive color and why many males are color-blind.

Our perceptual systems are able to perceive constancy in size, shape, and depth by utilizing monocular and binocular cues. Illusions are described as breaks or differences in what is expected. Optical illusions are dependent on our culture and early experiences. The Gestalt laws of organization are an attempt to explain how the whole is more than the sum of its parts. Gestaltists claim the brain imposes organization on stimuli by proximity, similarity, continuity, closure, and common fate.

Chapter 5 presents the basic components of sound and the structure of the ear and explains the place and frequency theories of hearing. *Psychology* explains how the direction of sounds is determined by time and intensity differences. Hearing impairments are possible at all ages.

Taste and smell are characterized as chemical senses and the role of smell in communication is explored in animals and humans. The skin senses of touch and pain are examined. The neuromatrix theory of pain and the body's use of endorphins are described as they relate to pain perception and management. Other perceptual senses such as kinesthesia, the vestibular sense, and extrasensory perception are also discussed.

Chapter 5 explains how complex each of our sensory systems is and how each relies on the brain to interpret information after it has been perceived. Our sensory systems convert physical energy into neural signals in much the same way your computer converts code into meaningful data.

# Chapter Objectives

- Investigate psychophysics by contrasting the theories of perceptual threshold with signal detection theory.

- Compare and contrast filter and attenuation theory as they relate to our ability to selectively attend to multiple stimuli.

- Discuss the known effects of a restricted environment and state recent applications for modifying human behavior.

- Identify and describe the parts of the eye and explain how each is related to the processing of visual stimuli.

- Characterize the relationship between the psychological and physical properties of color. Specifically, compare and contrast trichromatic opponent-process theories as they relate to color blindness.

- Explain how our visual perception system and experience allow us to maintain a uniform view of the world by means of size and shape constancy.

- Explain how monocular and binocular cues are associated with depth perception.

- Characterize some of the common illusions we experience and examine how perception may be culturally dependent.

- Discuss the Gestalt approach to conscious experience and describe five Gestalt laws of organization.

- Identify two physical and two psychological properties of sound. List and describe the parts of the ear and explain how each part functions to process auditory stimuli.

- Compare and contrast the place and frequency theories of hearing and evaluate how modern researchers utilize these theories together. And discuss the two key concepts involved in sound localization.

- Identify the four basic tastes and describe the phenomenon called sensory adaptation.

- Develop an understanding of olfaction in humans. Then investigate the research comparing communication and smell in humans and animals.

- Describe the structure and function of the skin and explain how a variety of sensations are perceived through touch.

- Examine pain as a perceptual system, outlining the neuromatrix theory and how endorphins are involved in pain control. Then evaluate the various new techniques in pain management.

# As you read...

## The Perceptual Experience

---
**5-1    Sensation and Perception: Definitions**
---

1.  Define Sensation.

2.  Define Perception.

3.  Define bottom-up analysis and top-down analysis.

4.  The sets of structures, functions and operations by means of which people perceive the world around them are called _____  _____.

---
**5-2    Psychophysics**
---

5.      Define Psychophysics.

6.      Define Threshold.

7.      What are absolute thresholds and difference thresholds?

8.      Describe three methods for studying perceptual thresholds.

9.      Researchers using Signal Detection Theory have found that varying _____ _____, _____ _____, and _____ all affect a person's willingness to say "Yes, I detect the signal".

10.     _____ _____ theory suggests that there are no finite or absolute thresholds, each response is individual.

11.     Define subliminal perception.

12.     Can you learn from subliminal perception? Why or why not?

13.     Define selective attention.


14.     What is the cocktail party phenomenon?


15.     Perceptual psychologists focus on _____ of a person's attention.


16.     Define and distinguish between filter theory and attenuation theory.


| 5-4 | Restricted Environmental Stimulation |

17.     Define and give an example of restricted environmental stimulation


18.     Give examples of positive effects of sensory restriction.


19.     Previous experience with sensory restriction may have a _____ effect, thereby increasing its effect with each experience.


| 5-5 | Inattentional Blindness |

20.     Define inattentional blindness.


21.     The more you pay attention to the _____ _____ the less likely you are to notice an _____ _____.


# The Visual System

1. Define electromagnetic radiation and its relation to the visual system.


2. List the 8 sections of the electromagnetic spectrum.

3.    Identify and describe the parts of the eye and explain how each is related to the processing of visual stimuli.

4.    Define Myopic and Hyperopic.

5.    Define photoreceptors.

6.    Light in the photoreceptor layer breaks down _____ which cause electrochemical change in the rod and cones.

7.    _____ or coding is the process by which stimuli is analyzed and converted into electrical impulses.

8.    Describe how information gets from the rods and cones to the brain.

9.    Describe the duplicity theory of vision.

10.    How are rods and cones functionally and structurally different?

11.    What is the visual acuity test and how do the cones affect it?

12.    When illumination levels change from high to low the increase in light sensitivity that occurs is called _____ _____ .

13.    What is the optic chiasm?

5-7    The Electrochemical Basis of Perception

14.    Define receptive fields.

15.    Define feature detectors and describe the 3 types of feature detectors?

16.    What other things are receptor fields associated with?

17.    Define parallel processing and serial processing.

| 5-8 | Eye Movements |
|---|---|

18.    Define Saccades.

19.    What are fixations?

20.    _____ _____ is the size of a region a person sees when fixating visually.

21.    What information do people use to determine the location of their next eye movement?

| 5-9 | Color Vision |
|---|---|

22.    What arc thc 3 psychological dimensions of color?

23.    The color of an object is referred to as _____, the _____ is how light or dark hue is and the purity of the color is known as _____.

24.    Define color coding

25.    Describe the trichromatic theory of color vision.

26.    What phenomena does the trichromatic theory of vision fail to explain?

27.    Define color blindness.

28.    Describe the opponent-process theory of color vision.

29.     People possessing normal color vision are called _____,
those who do not see any color are called _____

30.     How do dichromats see the world?


# Visual Perception

| 5-10     Perception of Form: Constancy |
|---|

1.  Define size constancy


2.  Define shape constancy


3.  What three variables determine the ability to maintain size constancy

| 5-11     Depth Perception |
|---|

4.      Define depth perception.


5.      Describe the following monocular depth cues
        A) Motion parallax _____

        B) Kinetic depth effect _____

        C) Linear perspective _____

        D) Interposition _____

        E) Texture _____

        F) Highlighting _____

        G) Atmospheric Perspective _____

        H) Accommodation _____


6.      List the two monocular depth cues that come from motion.

7.     What monocular depth cues come from the stimuli?


8.     Monocular and binocular cues are important in _____ perception.


9.     Describe the 2 main types of binocular depth cues



| 5-12 | Illusions |
|---|---|


10.    Define Illusion.


11.    Describe each of the following illusions and give an explanation of why each is thought to occur.
        A) Müller-Lyer _____

        B) Explanation _____

        C) Ponzo _____

        D) Explanation _____

        E) Moon illusion _____

        F) Explanation _____


12.    Describe how culture affects illusions.


13.    Define synethesia.


14.    Describe the results and conclusions of Ramachandran and Hubbard's study on colored number synethesia.



| 5-13 | Prosopagnosia: The Inability to Recognize Face |
|---|---|

15.    Define prosopagnosia.

16.    Define agnosia.

## 5-14    Gestalt Laws of Organization

17.    How did the early Gestalt psychologists believe people experience form and organization?

18.    Define the law of Pragnanz.

19.    Define figure and ground.

20.    Match the following laws of organization to the appropriate description:  proximity, similarity, continuity, common fate, closure.
   A) _____ Items that move or change together are seen as a whole.
   B) _____ Parts of a figure that are left out will be filled in by the perceptual system.
   C) _____ Groups are formed by elements close to one another in space and time.
   D) _____ A string of items indicates where the next item will be found.
   E) _____ Similar items tend to be perceived in groups.

21.    Identify the perceptual process that best explains why each of the following situations is perceived by the observer as described.

  *monocular depth cue*    *illusion*
  *binocular depth cue*    *Gestalt laws organization*

   A) _____ A basket of fruit and a bottle of wine are positioned in such a way that the basket blocks part of the image of the wine bottle; as a result the observer perceives the wine bottle as being closer.
   B) _____ As you move your new record album closer to your face so that you can read the song titles, a series of muscles attached to the crystalline lenses in your eyes change the shape of the lenses and keep the image on your retinas in focus.
   C) _____ As your lover moves closer to you to establish intimate eye contact, your eyes converge, moving toward one another and providing you with necessary depth cues.

D) _____ An auditorium is filled with folding chairs that are either gray or blue. They are set up in sections by color beginning with ten rows of blue chairs, then rows of gray chairs, another ten rows of blue chairs and so on. As an observer, you perceive the chairs in groups by the similarity of their color.

E) _____ As you look at your favorite painting you notice the darker objects seem to be farther away than the lighter objects.

F) _____ You look at two lines, one of which appears to be longer. When you measure the two lines you find that they are the same length. Yet, when you look at them again one of the lines still appears to be longer.

G) _____ The cowboy on a sign outside of "Joe's Place" appears to be waving at you because the light bulbs that make up the sign blink in a synchronized manner.

# Hearing

**5-15    Sound**

1. Define sound.

2. Two psychological aspects of sound are _____ and _____.

3. Define frequency.

4. Define pitch.

5. High pitched tones usually have _____ frequencies.

6. Define amplitude.

7. _____ is a measure of amplitude.

8. The specific mixture of frequencies and amplitude that make up sound is called _____.

9.    Define audition.

10.    List the 3 major parts of the ear

11.    Where is the eardrum (tympanic membrane) located and what does it do?

12.    Why is the rate of dyslexia different in America and Italy?

13.    Define orthography.

14.    Describe the parts of the middle ear and their functions.

15.    The middle ear is made up of _____ known as the hammer, anvil, and stirrup.

16.    Describe the parts of the inner ear.

17.    Different areas of the _____ _____ in the cochlea are stimulated by different frequencies.

18.    _____ _____ initiate the electrical coding of sound waves.

19.    Describe the route of nerve impulses in the brain's auditory system.

20.    Match the following structures of the ear with the appropriate description:  external ear, middle ear, inner ear.
   A) _____ The snail-like tube where pressure changes, received by the basilar membrane, stimulates hair cells and brings about the initial electrical coding in the nervous system of sound waves.  This structure is also known as the cochlea.
   B) _____ The fleshy tissue on the outside of the head and the opening that leads to the eardrum.
   C) _____ The eardrum and tiny bones that amplify sound waves and stimulate the basilar membrane

## 5-17 Theories of Hearing

1.  Describe the two major classes of hearing theories.

2.  What are the limitations of the place theory?

3.  Give an example of a problem with the frequency theory.

## 5-18 Sound Localization

4.  Describe the 2 key factors that influence sound localization.

5.  The interaural time and interaural intensity differences are analyzed by the brain to determine _____ _____.

6.  How do you localize sound when it is in front of you?

## 5-19 Hearing Impairments

7.  Define Conduction deafness.

8.  Define Sensorineural deafness.

9.  Exposure to very high intensity sound for prolonged periods can lead to _____ deafness.

10.  What is an audiogram?

# Taste and Smell

## 5-20 Taste

1.  Describe the parts of the tongue.

2. _____ is a chemical sense.

3. List the 4 basic tastes.

4. Define sensory adaptation.

**5-21    Smell**

5.    Define olfaction.

6.    Describe the olfactory epithelium, olfactory receptor cells, and olfactory bulbs and how they process odors.

7.    Describe the 3 levels of smells in perfumes

8.    The sensory stimulus and the frequency and intensity of _____ _____ all influence smell and taste.

**5-22    Smell and Communication**

9.    Define Pheromones.

10.    Give 3 examples of how animals use pheromones to communicate and elicit behavior.

11.    Due to chemical signals menstrual cycles of women who live together for several months become _____.

## The Skin Senses

1.  List the 3 skin senses.

2.  Information from the _____ _____ is ultimately sent to the somatosensory cortex.

## 5-23 Touch

3. List and describe the 3 layers of the skin.

4. The cells of the _____ are replaced approximately every 28 days.

5. Why can't people tickle themselves?

## 5-24 Pain

6. What types of stimuli do psychologists use to study pain?

7. Define free nerve endings.

8. Define neuromatrix theory.

9. List the 5 inputs that act on the neuromatrix programs.

10. Define endorphins.

11. _____ is an endorphin that blocks the pain signals in the brain.

12. Describe acupuncture.

13. 15-20% of highly suggestible find relief from pain through _____.

14. Give examples of other ways to manage pain.

## 5-25 Kinesthesis and the Vestibular Sense

15. Define kinethesis.

16.     Sensory cues that come from with the body are called _____ _____.

17.     Describe the vestibular sense.

18.     Define telepathy.


19.     Define clairvoyance.


20.     _____ is the ability to predict future events.


21.     _____ is one's ability to move objects by mental powers.

| | |
|---|---|
| Sensation | Opponent-Process Theory |
| Perception | Trichromats |
| Psychophysics | Monochromats |
| Absolute Threshold | Dichromats |
| Signal Detection Theory | Size Constancy |
| Subliminal Perception. | Shape Constancy |
| Electromagnetic Radiation | Monocular Depth Cues |
| Light | Accommodation |
| Myopic | Binocular Depth Cues |
| Hyperopic | Retinal Disparity |
| Photoreceptors | Convergence |
| Transduction | Illusion |
| Visual Cortex | Law of Pragnanz |
| Dark Adaptation | Sound |
| Optic Chiasm | Frequency |
| Receptive Fields | Pitch |
| Agnosia | Amplitude |
| Saccades | Conduction Deafness |
| Hue | Sensorineural Deafness |
| Brightness | Olfaction |
| Saturation | Endorphins |
| Trichromatic Theory | Kinethesis |
| Color Blindness | Vestibular Sense |

# After you read . . . Self Test

## Chapter 5 Self Test

1. Perception: (144)
   A. allows us to experience and adapt to our environment.
   B. is a complex process of receiving and interpreting stimuli.
   C. allows sensory input to acquire meaning.
   D. all of the above

2. The relationship between a person's conscious experience of a stimulus and the physical properties of a stimulus is the focus of: (145)
   A. transduction.
   B. perception.
   C. sensation.
   D. psychophysics.

3. The human eye works very much like a: (151)
   A. microscope.
   B. telescope.
   C. camera.
   D. prism.

4. The part of the eye that contains rods and cones is called the: (151)
   A. retina.
   B. iris.
   C. cornea.
   D. bipolar layer.

5. The brain can process two sets of signals about a particular image and allows us to see form and depth because impulses cross to the opposite side of the brain when they reach the: (153)
   A. optic chiasm.
   B. lateral geniculate nucleus.
   C. striate cortex.
   D. none of the above

6. We can discriminate between a circle and a triangle because each shape: (155)
   A. is clearly different from any other shape.
   B. stimulates the cells of different receptive fields.
   C. passes through a different portion of the crystalline lens.
   D. is recognized by the primary visual cortex.

7. In Hirsch and Spinelli's study, the cats whose early visual experience was limited to horizontal lines: (154)
   A. were able to see lines in all angles when the experimental goggles were removed.
   B. bumped into vertical objects, such as chair legs, after the goggles had been removed.
   C. became overwhelmed by too much visual stimulation when the goggles were removed.
   D. could see vertical lines, but ignored them since they had no experience with them.

8. Which of the following objects best illustrates the property of color called "saturation?" (158-159)
   A. a pink carnation
   B. a blue sapphire
   C. a green olive
   D. a red brick

9. The ability to make all colors by mixing three basic colors, red, blue, and green is part of the:
   A. opponent-process theory. (159)
   B. Law of Similarity.
   C. Trichromatic theory.
   D. Law of Proximity.

10. The opponent process theory assumes that: (159)
   A. there are three types of receptors, each maximally sensitive to one group of wavelengths.
   B. that three sets of receptors respond positively or negatively to different wavelengths.
   C. color coding occurs at the retina.
   D. A and C

11. Persons who are totally color blind would be considered: (160)
   A. monochromats.
   B. trichromats.
   C. dichromats.
   D. anomolous trichromats.

12. You perceive a book as having the same shape whether you see it from the side or from the front because of a perceptual process known as: (162)
   A. similarity.
   B. accommodation.
   C. interposition.
   D. constancy.

13. Retinal disparity: (164)
   A. is most likely to occur when objects are far away.
   B. is greatest when images on the retina are the farthest apart.
   C. keeps information on corresponding points on the retina.
   D. is a monocular depth cue.

14. Two horizontal lines of same length surrounded by slanted lines is a: (165)
   A.   Ponzo Illusion.
   B.   Moon Illusion.
   C.   Muller-Lyer Illusion.
   D.   none of the above

15. Elements close to one another in space or time will be perceived as groups in the Law of: (169)
   A.   Common Fate Principles.
   B.   Similarity.
   C.   Proximity.
   D.   Continuity.

16. Which of the following is the physical attribute of loudness? (171)
   A.   frequency
   B.   amplitude
   C.   pitch
   D.   tone

17. The cochlea is: (172)
   A.   part of the middle ear.
   B.   the fleshy tissue on the outside of the head that we usually refer to as the ear.
   C.   a snaillike tube where hair cells are stimulated by a change in sound pressure.
   D.   A and C

18. Which of the following statements is *true*? (172)
   A.   Auditory cells are maximally sensitive to certain narrow ranges of frequencies.
   B.   Frequency theories seem to be much more accurate than place theories in providing an explanation for how we hear.
   C.   One Hertz (Hz) is equal to ten cycles per second.
   D.   Hair cells in the cochlea stimulate the basilar membrane.

19. Taste receptors are _____ found on the tongue. (175)
   A.   the papillae
   B.   the "moats"
   C.   the taste buds
   D.   in the saliva

20. The_____ allows you to touch your finger to your nose with your eyes closed. (183)
   A.   sense of touch
   B.   vestibular sense
   C.   kinesthesis sense
   D.   optical alignment sense

21. An extrasensory process by which thought is transferred from one person to another without the use of normal communications is: (184)
    A. transference.
    B. telepathy.
    C. clairvoyance.
    D. precognition.

22. Adult human skin measures roughly _____ yards and is made up of _____ layers. (178)
    A. 3-3
    B. 2-2
    C. 2-3
    D. 3-2

23. What is the name of the bulging, transparent, protective layer covering the front of the eye? (151)
    A. pupil
    B. lens
    C. iris
    D. cornea

24. What is another name for nearsightedness? (151)
    A. hypermetropic
    B. myopic
    C. prebyopic
    D. none of the above

25. The part of your eye in which you have mostly rods is: (151-152)
    A. the top half of your retina.
    B. your fovea.
    C. the center of your retina.
    D. the outer edge of your retina.

26. Name the type of eye movements being made as you read this statement. (157)
    A. saccadic
    B. random
    C. vergence
    D. pursuit eye

27. A color with low saturation is (158-159)
    A. green.
    B. pink.
    C. blue.
    D. yellow.

28. Where are the true sensory receptors for sound located? (172)
    A.   cochlea
    B.   occipital lobe
    C.   eardrum
    D.   retina

29. The factor that seems to play the biggest role in sensorineural deafness is: (174)
    A.   life-long exposure to excessive noise.
    B.   birth defects.
    C.   aging.
    D.   disease.

30. Where on the tongue should a sourball be placed in order to maximize the sensation of sour? (176-177)
    A.   back
    B.   side
    C.   middle
    D.   front

31. An absolute threshold is (145)
    A.   a statistically determined minimum level of stimulation needed to excite a perceptual system.
    B.   the smallest amount of change in a stimulus needed for most people to detect the change.
    C.   a relatively permanent change in the level of sensitivity in a sense organ due to experience.
    D.   the shortest amount of time a stimulus can exist before it will be detected by the perceptual system.

32. The theory of selective attention that states that all incoming information is analyzed, but only certain information is chosen to be passed on to higher levels for more complex processing, is called the (148)
    A.   localization theory.
    B.   filter theory.
    C.   attenuation theory.
    D.   threshold theory.

33. When a sense organ processes stimuli and converts them into electrical impulses, it is called. (151)
    A.   lateralization.
    B.   localization.
    C.   papillation.
    D.   transduction.

34. The experiment with kittens raised to see only one kind of line who, as adult cats, were unable to see any other kinds of lines supports which view of the visual system? (154)
    A.   Biological factors have no effect on our ability to see; it is completely controlled by our experience.
    B.   Biological abilities are present from birth, but without proper experience they do not develop normally.
    C.   Experience has no effect on our ability to see; it is completely controlled by biological factors.
    D.   The biological structures we need to see are created as a result of our experience.

35. In the opponent-process theory of color, our experience of a color is controlled by (159)
    A.   its position on three dimensions (red-green, blue-yellow, black-white).
    B.   the relative activations of three different kinds of cones (red, green, and blue).
    C.   the frequency of firing in the optic nerve, corresponding to the frequency of the light.
    D.   an automatic process that triggers the opposite color for any wavelength of light.

36. An object that is moving appears more three-dimensional than one that is perfectly still. This is called the _____ effect. (162)
    A.   visual motion
    B.   shape constancy
    C.   optical localization
    D.   kinetic depth

37. Cross-cultural research on the perception of illusions indicates that people whose culture does not include many straight lines or sharp corners will (166)
    A.   have more trouble seeing many illusions.
    B.   be fooled more easily by many illusions.
    C.   be unable to interpret the pictures at all.
    D.   see the illusions exactly as Americans do.

38. The three major parts of the ear are the (171)
    A.   hammer, anvil, and stirrup.
    B.   timbre, pitch, and loudness detectors.
    C.   rods, cones, and hair cells.
    D.   outer ear, middle ear, and inner ear.

39. The first bite of Joe's soup seemed very salty. After eating continuously for several minutes, it seemed less salty. This is probably due to the phenomenon of (176)
    A.   sensory overload.
    B.   chemical deterioration.
    C.   sensory adaptation.
    D.   gustatory amnesia.

40. When a police officer asks a suspected drunk driver "How many fingers do you see?" it is a test of vision. When the officer asks the driver to touch his finger to the tip of his nose with his eyes closed, which sense is being tested? (183)
    A. Kinesthesis
    B. Olfaction
    C. Gustation
    D. Orientation

41. When an incoming stimulus is interpreted and acquires meaning, it is called: (144)
    A. threshold
    B. adaptation
    C. sensation
    D. perception

42. The photoreceptors for the visual system are contained in the: (151)
    A. lens
    B. retina
    D. iris
    C. cornea

43. When a person describes their car is red, they are describing the psychological dimension of hue. Which physical dimension corresponds to hue? (158)
    A. wavelength
    B. intensity
    C. purity
    D. saturation

44. In the auditory system, transduction occurs at the: (172)
    A. ear drum
    B. cochlea
    C. outer ear
    D. ossicles

45. Sensorineural deafness results from damage to the: (174)
    A. ear drum
    B. ossicles
    C. tympanic membrane
    D. cochlea

# When You Have Finished

## Essay Questions

1. Compare and contrast top-down and bottom-up analysis. (144-145)

2. Taste and smell are chemical senses. Identify and discuss things that influence taste and smell beyond the chemical stimulant. (176-178)

3. What is the evolutionary perspective on gender differences in spatial processing? (156-157)

4. Describe the research on sensory deprivation and what it indicates about expectations. (148-149)

5. Define prosopagnosia and what research about it has told us about the visual system. (166-169)

# Chapter 6

# Consciousness

## Before you read...

Consciousness refers to our awareness of our environment and our awareness of our own thoughts, feelings, and memories. Consciousness can be seen as a continuum from alertness to dreaming, hypnosis, or drug-induced states as levels from total awareness to unresponsiveness. In either case, psychologists study consciousness because of its obvious relationship with our awareness of our environment and its potential to affect behavior.

The most widely studied state or level of consciousness is sleep. Circadian rhythms regulate the sleep-wakefulness cycle, which can easily be altered by job duties, travel, and other interruptions to our daily routine. Sleep is a natural state of consciousness, but the reason for sleep remains unclear. One of the stages, called REM (rapid eye movement) appears to be critical for normal daily functioning. When we are deprived of REM sleep, we become anxious and irritable, have difficulty concentrating, and do worse on tests that involve attention and original responses. Sleep disorders are examined.

Sigmund Freud described dreams as the royal road to the unconscious. Dreams have played an important role in psychology almost since the beginning. Dreams occur largely during REM sleep and may include vivid visual, auditory, or tactile imagery. The content of dreams remains a hot topic in psychology as well as in popular literature and the media, but recent research suggests that dreams may be a random collection of images and therefore have little or no importance.

Consciousness can be controlled and modified by biofeedback, hypnosis, or meditation. Each of these methods has had some success in treating problems such as headaches, high blood pressure, stress-related illness, pain management, and memory loss. However, each method is not without its critics.

In addition, conscious experience can be altered by drugs. Lefton and Brannon point out that we live in a drug-using culture with numerous legal and illegal drugs readily available for all ages. Dependence and tolerance are defined and a description of a substance abuser is given. One of the most pervasive examples of drug abuse is alcoholism. Lefton and Brannon outline the effects of alcohol on individuals, society, and public safety. The risk factors for alcoholism and familial patterns are examined.

# Chapter Objectives

- Develop an understanding of the continuum of consciousness from alertness through altered states of consciousness.

- Understand the different views and theories of consciousness.

- Develop an understanding of circadian rhythms and be able to give examples of how they affect human behavior.

- Characterize sleep through developing an understanding of sleep cycles and stages.

- Understand the brain chemicals that affect when we are sleepy.

- List and describe the major sleep disorders.

- Outline the physiological processes that are involved with dreams and develop an understanding of the frequency of dreams and factors affecting the recall of a dream.

- Understand what impacts dream content and what lucid dreaming is.

- Compare and contrast the dream theories of Freud, Jung, and activation synthesis.

- Examine biofeedback and critically evaluate its effectiveness in helping people manage physiological problems.

- Describe the effects of hypnosis and discuss the challenges presented by Barber as an alternative explanation for the effects of hypnosis.

- Describe the two types of meditation and investigate possible uses in altering physiological responses.

- Identify the different types of psychoactive drugs and their actions.

- State the three criteria for substance abuse and have a clear understanding of the terms psychological dependence, withdrawal, and tolerance as they relate to drug use and abuse

- Develop an understanding of why people abuse drugs.

# As you read...

## Consciousness

### 6-1    Defining Consciousness

1.  Define Consciousness.

2.  What is dualism?

3.  Define materialism (reductionism).

4.  An _____  _____ is the dramatically different state of consciousness different from ordinary awareness and responsiveness.

5.  Define metacognition.

### 6-2    Theories of Consciousness

6.   What do the mysterians think about consciousness?

7.   Describe what the materialists say about consciousness.

8.   What is the Pinker's view of consciousness?

9.   Subjective experiences and a person's awareness and feelings is referred to as _____.

10.   Define access.

11.   What is self-knowledge?

12.    Unlike sentience, _____ and _____ can be analyzed because they are cognitive activities.

13.    How does Chalmers view consciousness?

# Sleep

1.  Define circadian rhythms.

2.  What are 2 situations that affect the circadian rhythm?

3.  What can be done to minimize the adjustment process?

4.    What is an EEG?

5.    _____ is height of the waves and _____ is the number of waves per second.

6.    Define REM sleep.

7.    Define NREM sleep.

8.    Describe the 5 stages of sleep.

9.    A person can dream in _____ stage (s) of sleep.

10.    In the deepest stage of sleep, stage 4, even high amplitude brain wave traces are called _____ _____.

## 6-5    Sleep Deprivation

11.    Describe of the problems Randy Gardner had during his 11 days of sleep deprivation.

12.    In the United States _____ % of adults do not get enough sleep.

13.    Driving skills are impaired after only _____ hours of missed sleep.

14.    Describe the results of the study of long-haul truckers and sleep.

15.    Define sleep debt.

## 6-6    Why Do We Sleep?

16.    Does sleep serve a restorative function?

17.    What does the evolutionary approach say about why we sleep?

18.    Describe the 2 camps on the importance of REM sleep.

## 6-7    Is There a Sleep Switch?

19.    What is the VLPO and how is it involved in sleep?

20.    How is the suprachiasmic nucleus involved in sleep?

## 6-8    Sleep Disorders

21.    Define narcolepsy.

22.    How is sleep apnea treated?

23.     What problems are associated with the use of barbiturates as sleeping aids?


24.     What is sleepwalking?


25.     Match the following sleep disorders with the appropriate description.
        *narcolepsy     sleep apnea     insomnia        night terrors*
        A) _____ People with this disorder stop breathing for at least fifteen
        seconds up to as many as 100 times a night.  During the day they are very
        sleepy, may have memory losses, work related accidents, and severe
        headaches.
        B) _____ This disorder is especially common in children between the ages
        of 3 and 8.  The symptoms involve sitting up abruptly in a state of shear fright,
        screaming, and breathing quickly.
        C) _____ This is a common disorder often caused by anxiety or depression
        where a person has a prolonged inability to fall asleep.
        D) _____ People with this disorder could have difficulty on the job or
        when driving a car because they suddenly and unexpectedly fall asleep.


## Dreams

| 6-9    What is a Dream? |
|---|

1. What are dreams?


2. What percentage of people woken from REM sleep report a dream?


3. Approximately 90 minutes after a person falls asleep the first _____ period occurs.


| 6-10   Content of Dreams |
|---|

4.      What are some common dream themes?


5.      Unlike other visual areas of the brain the _____ is nearly shut down
during REM sleep.

6.      What are lucid dreams?

7.  Discuss the following researchers' positions on dreaming.
    A.   Freud _____
         1. Manifest content _____
         2. Latent content _____
    B.   Jung _____
         _____

    C.   Hobson and McCarley

         _____
         _____
         _____

8.   What is the collective unconscious?

9.   Define archetypes.

10.  In Jung's view, the archetype _____ represents a person's inner striving for unity.

11.  What is the cognitive view on dreaming?

12.  What does cross-cultural research show about dreams of children?

13.  What is a descriptive study?

14.  What are the results and conclusions of Louie and Wilson's research with rats?

## Controlling Consciousness: Biofeedback, Hypnosis, and Meditation

**6-12    Biofeedback**

1.   Define biofeedback.

2.   What did Miller's research contribute to biofeedback?

3. List some disorder's that biofeedback has been used to treat?

| 6-13 | **Hypnosis** |

4.     Define hypnotic induction.

5.     What are the three views of hypnosis?

6.     What 2 qualities does a good hypnotic subject have?

7.     Define suggestibility.

8.     The person's willingness to follow the instructions of the hypnotist is called suggestibility or _____  _____.

| 6-14 | **Meditation** |

9.     Define meditation.

10.    In what areas do probationers benefit from forced meditation?

11.    There are two types of meditation: _____ and
_____.

12.    What evidence is given that meditation is not just relaxation?

## Altering Consciousness with Drugs

1. What is a drug?

2. Define psychoactive drugs.

3.      Define tolerance.


4.      _____ occurs when a person discontinues taking a drug they have developed a _____ for.

5.      Define addiction.


## 6-15    Psychoactive Drugs

6.      What is the blood-brain barrier?


7.      _____ _____ affect the brain's neural transmissions and chemicals to induce an altered state of consciousness.

8.      Define sedative-hypnotics (depressants).


9.      Describe the effects of alcohol.


10.     _____ are a class of drugs that reduce pain, calm, are addictive, and produce tolerance.


11.     What are endorphins?


12.     Define stimulants.


13.     List and describe 4 stimulants.


14.     Define psychedelic.


15.     What is MDMA?


16.     _____ is the active ingredient in marijuana (cannabis sativa).

17.    Describe how marijuana affects people.

18.    Which two substances constitute the biggest drug problems in the United States?


19.    What is a good way to determine use vs abuse?


20.    List the 3 things that indicate someone is a substance abuser.


21.    Match the following terms to the appropriate definition.
       *dependence*            *tolerance*                *withdrawal symptoms*
       A) _____ Reliance on regular use of a drug, without which the individual
       suffers a psychological and/or physiological reaction.
       B) _____ A variety of physiological reactions that occur when a person
       who has developed a physiological dependence to a drug no longer takes the
       drug.
       C) _____ A progressive insensitivity to repeated use of a drug in the same
       dose.  A user must have increasingly greater amounts of the drug to achieve
       the desired high.

22.    What does Lesher think is a component of drug addiction?


23.    Describe how dopamine is involved in drug addiction.


24.    Define genetic predisposition.

**Term Identification: Make flashcards for each of the following terms. Hint: Use the definitions in the margins of the chapter**

Consciousness

Circadian Rhythms

Sleep

Electroencephalogram (EEG)

Non-Rapid Eye Movement (NREM) sleep

Rapid Eye Movement (REM) sleep

Insomnia

Dream

Lucid Dream

Manifest Content

Latent Content

Collective Unconscious

Biofeedback

Meditation

Drug

Psychoactive Drug

Tolerance

Dependence

Blood-Brain Barrier

Psychological Dependence

Alcoholic

Sedative-Hypnotic

Opiate

Stimulant

Psychedelic

Substance Abuser

Withdrawal Symptoms

# After you read . . . Self Test

## Chapter 6 Self Test

1.  The beginnings of the concept of dualism is most closely associated with (191)
    A.   Stephen Pinket
    B.   John Watson
    C.   Sigmund Freud
    D.   Rene Descartes

2.  According to Daniel Dennett, the brain: (192)
    A.   creates multiple drafts of experience which are constantly being reanalyzed.
    B.   is busy deleting extraneous information and experience from storage.
    C.   operates out of the active and receptive modes proposed by Ornstein.
    D.   all of the above

3.  Circadian rhythms control all except: (193)
    A.   yawning.
    B.   bodily rhythms.
    C.   body temperature.
    D.   sleep patterns.

4.  Subjective experience and awareness is termed (192)
    A.   emotion
    B.   access
    C.   sentience
    D.   self-knowledge

5.  Jet lag and irregular work shifts are problems for individuals and society because they contribute to (194)
    A.   increasing separation of human society from the natural world
    B.   disruptions of the circadian rhythms, leading to reduced efficiency
    C.   feelings of powerlessness, isolation, and disorientation
    D.   poor nutrition as a result of grabbing irregular meals

6.  A function of the ventrolateral preoptic area of the hypothalamus may be that of a (200)
    A.   anxiety interpretation center
    B.   hunger center controlled by visual stimuli
    C.   sleep switch
    D.   sexual orientation center

7.  People who fall asleep suddenly at inappropriate times may have a sleep disorder called (200)
    A.   sleep apnea.
    B.   insomnia.
    C.   night terrors.
    D.   narcolepsy.

8. Night terrors are a sleep disorder that mainly affects children and that involves (201)
   A.   frequently experiencing vivid, powerful bad dreams
   B.   intense feelings of terror not associated with any dreams
   C.   the desire to sleep with the parents to avoid "monsters"
   D.   being afraid to fall asleep for fear of not waking up again

9. During REM dreams, a person experiences (202)
   A.   a relaxed brain state and rapid body movements
   B.   powerful feelings of fear and terror
   C.   sleep spindles and K complexes.
   D.   vivid visual imagery and a lack of body movements.

10. A dream in which a person is aware that she is dreaming while the dream is being experienced is called a (203)
    A.   NREM dream
    B.   lucid dream
    C.   hypnogogic
    D.   spritual

11. In Jung's theory of dreams, the storehouse of ideas and images inherited from our ancestors is called the (204)
    A.   latent content
    B.   manifest content
    C.   mandala archetype
    D.   collective unconscious

12. Which of the following has been used to provide an explanation for substance use and abuse? (211)
    A.   societal factors
    B.   individual family situations
    C.   genetic heritage and medical problems
    D.   all of the above

13. When we say a person has gained a tolerance to a drug, we mean that the person: (211)
    A.   can take a drug without suffering from any negative side effects.
    B.   can take a minimum amount of a drug without experiencing withdrawal symptoms.
    C.   no longer experiences the desired effect from that particular amount of a drug.
    D.   has become addicted to a drug.

14. The following is NOT mentioned in the cognitive view of dream theory? (204)
    A.   dreams are connected to reality
    B.   dreams reflect issues with which a person is dealing
    C.   dreams have meaning
    D.   dreams have a deep hidden meaning

15. Alcohol is classified as a _____ drug. (211)
    A.  sedative-hypnotic
    B.  narcotic
    C.  psychostimulant
    D.  psychedelic

16. According to the activation-synthesis theory of dreams, a dream is the result of (204-205)
    A.  unacceptable impulses buried in the unconscious.
    B.  ideas and images we inherited from our ancestors.
    C.  trying to make sense of random brain activity.
    D.  unstable fluctuations in the sleep centers of the brain.

17. Meditation is a state of consciousness that is characterized by (209)
    A.  concentration and deep relaxation
    B.  lack of awareness of one's environment
    C.  giving control to another person.
    D.  information about bodily processes

18. A drug that alters a person's behavior, thoughts, or emotions through its effects on the nervous system is called a(n) _____ drug. (210-211)
    A.  addictive
    B.  abusive
    C.  neurological
    D.  psychoactive

19. A major psychological effect of alcohol is that it acts as a (211)
    A.  stimulant and makes us overactive
    B.  depressant, and reduces our inhibitions
    C.  tranquilizer, and makes us feel fearful
    D.  aggressor, and makes us more violent

20. Many researchers assert that _____ keeps people addicted to heroin and other addictive drugs. (216)
    A.  the biological reinforcing quality of the drug
    B.  a lack of will power
    C.  social pressure
    D.  poor nutrition

21. Opiates are drugs that produce (212-213)
    A.  pain relief and addiction
    B.  sleep and depression
    C.  excitement and hallucinations
    D.  intoxication and hyperactivity

22. Which of the following drugs alters consciousness, affects moods, thoughts, memory and perception, and is considered a psychedelic? (214)
    A.   cocaine
    B.   crack
    C.   marijuana
    D.   crank

23. John B. Watson and other early behaviorists did not believe that consciousness was an appropriate subject for psychologists to study because: (190)
    A.   it invalidates research done with animals.
    B.   it is not observable and measurable.
    C.   the elements of consciousness had not been identified.
    D.   individual differences in consciousness are too large.

24. What do researchers use to study changes in brain wave activity during sleep? (195)
    A.   electroencephalogram
    B.   positron oscilloscope
    C.   electromyogram
    D.   electroculogram

25. Why has REM sleep been referred to as "paradoxical sleep?" (196)
    A.   It has little or no restorative value.
    B.   There is a great deal of body movement.
    C.   The EEG resembles that of an aware person.
    D.   The sleeper is aware of environmental stimuli.

26. A sleep disorder in which an individual stops breathing for several seconds during sleep is called: (200)
    A.   apnea.
    B.   night terrors.
    C.   hypersomnia.
    D.   somnambulism.

27. What aspect of dreams was emphasized by Freud? (203)
    A.   the use of symbolism
    B.   the role of environmental stimuli in dream content
    C.   their relationship to physiological variables
    D.   their function in the organization of memory

28. For which disorders have biofeedback procedures been most frequently used? (206-207)
    A.   digestive
    B.   hereditary
    C.   stress-related
    D.   mental

29. The main reason why people use cocaine is because it (213)
    A.   helps them relax and calm down
    B.   makes them more creative and imaginitive
    C.   produces and intense feeling of pleasure
    D.   has no known physical side effects

30. When an individual requires progressively more and more of a drug to get the same effect, that individual has developed drug: (211)
    A. tolerance
    B. antipathy
    C. immunity
    D. insensitivity

31. Ecstasy was designed from (213)
    A. LSD
    B. methamphetamine
    C. cocaine
    D. methatrexate

32. Which of the following drugs produce the most marked shifts in consciousness? (213)
    A. cocaine
    B. stimulants
    C. the opiates
    D. the hallucinogens

33. Access is (192)
    A. the ability to recognize the uniqueness of experiences
    B. the awareness of a pattern in the rhythms of one's life
    C. the awareness of subjective experience
    D. the ability to report on the end products of thought

34. What stage of sleep has over 50% delta waves (196)
    A. REM
    B. Stage 2
    C. Stage 3
    D. Stage 4

35. REM sleep is often called paradoxical sleep because (196)
    A. no one knows what purpose it serves.
    B. it occurs at unpredictable times during the night.
    C. it is in some ways deep and in some ways active.
    D. some people experience it but others don't.

36. It is typical for people to have _____ full sleep cycles during an 8-hour period and for each cycle to last about _____ minutes (195)
    A. two; 240
    B. three; 150
    C. seven; 40
    D. five; 90

37. The proportion of REM to NREM sleep is greatest for (196)
    A. adolescents
    B. newborns
    C. elderly people
    D. young children

113

38. Biofeedback is a technique that allows individuals to (206)
    A.  gain control over the content of their dreams.
    B.  alter the patterns of their sleep cycles.
    C.  interpret the true meanings of their dreams.
    D.  control some of the body's involuntary responses.

39. Insomnia is defined as (201)
    A.  the inability to sleep and breathe at the same time
    B.  falling asleep suddenly and unexpectedly during the day
    C.  a prolonged inability to fall asleep or stay asleep
    D.  sudden feelings of terror at night when not dreaming

40. When you tell another person about a dream you have had, Freud would say you are reporting the _____ of your dream (203)
    A.  superficial aspect
    B.  manifest content
    C.  ulterior theme
    D.  latent content

41. Cross-cultural studies of dream content discovered (204)
    A.  a person's environment played no role in dream content
    B.  dreams incorporated basic cultural views of the purpose of dreaming
    C.  a person's environment was more important than their cultural view
    D.  a person's cultural view was more important than his or her environment

42. According to Barber's research on hypnosis, what is the special factor in hypnotic induction that allows hypnotized subjects to perform much better at many tasks than nonhypnotized people? (207)
    A.  It creates a unique state of consciousness, a trance state
    B.  It gives the hypnotist unusual control over the subject
    C.  Nothing; hypnosis works no better than task-motivating instructions
    D.  It brings the subject closer to his or her unconscious mind

43. When a person is conscious of, or thinks about, their own thought processes, it is called: (191)
    A.  consciousness
    B.  altered consciousness
    C.  metacognition
    D.  self consciousness

44. Donald briefly stops breathing while he sleeps, sometimes as often as 100 times per night. Which sleep disorder does he probably have? (200)
    A.  insomnia
    B.  sleep apnea
    C.  narcolepsy
    D.  night terrors

45. Sharon is learning to relax her heart in order to lower her blood pressure. This method of monitoring and controlling involuntary activity is called: (206)
   A.   meditation
   B.   hypnotic induction
   C.   biofeedback
   D.   medication

# When You Have Finished

## Essay Questions

1. What does cross-cultural research demonstrate about sleep patterns? (196-197)

2. How might the brain's reward system contribute to drug abuse? (215-218)

3. What has cross-cultural research with children told us about dreams? (202-205)

4. What 3 things indicate that a person is a substance abuser and what are withdrawal symptoms? (215-216)

5. Describe the brain activity during sleepwalking and who is most likely to have this sleep disorder. (201)

# Chapter 7

# Learning

## Before you read...

Humans differentiate themselves from animals by their ability to learn complex behaviors. *Psychology* defines and describes the three basic learning processes of classical conditioning, operant conditioning, and cognitive learning. Pavlov's accidental discovery of the process of classical conditioning has led researchers to uncover many human behaviors that are learned. Behaviors such as emotions can be learned through association. Reflexive behaviors can be paired with other behaviors to create a chain of higher order learning. Complex behaviors can be extinguished, as well using the principles of classical conditioning. Also, the effectiveness of classical conditioning may depend on factors such as timing and the strength of the unconditioned stimulus.

*"As a result of..."* This phrase summarizes what B. F. Skinner thought about learning. According to Skinner, behaviors are acquired and maintained <u>as a result of</u> some consequence following the behavior. This process is termed <u>operant conditioning</u> and relies on the principles of reinforcement and punishment. Put simply, behaviors will increase when reinforced and decrease when punishment is the consequence. Like classical conditioning, operant conditioning is influenced by many variables, such as the nature of reinforcers, schedules of reinforcement and stimulus discrimination and generalization. Intrinsically motivated behaviors and their resistance to conditioning are discussed. Practical applications for behavioral regulation are also presented.

All behaviors cannot be explained by association or consequences. Cognitive variables like insight, latent learning, and generative learning focus on the thinking process and thoughts that establish and maintain behaviors. Lefton and Brannon describe a learning-to-learn model that provides an interesting approach to study habits. Finally, observational learning theory illustrates how we learn by watching models. As in other learning models, the effectiveness of observational learning depends on several important elements surrounding the model as well as the observer.

The remaining chapters of *Psychology* rely on your understanding the concepts of learning. If you spend a little extra time on this chapter, you will benefit from your efforts.

# Chapter Objectives

- Describe classical conditioning and define the types of stimuli and responses involved.

- Explain how classical conditioning is used to elicit behavioral and emotional responses in humans. Discuss higher order conditioning and detail at least two factors that determine the extent of conditioning.

- Explain the importance of strength, timing, and frequency of classical conditioning processes. Explain how the concept of predictability is related to classical conditioning.

- Describe how classically conditioned responses undergo extinction and then recur through spontaneous recovery. Describe the concepts stimulus generalization and stimulus discrimination as they relate to classical conditioning.

- Define operant conditioning and discuss two American psychologists who contributed greatly to our understanding of this type of learning. Explain how shaping is used in operant conditioning and why it is an effective teaching tool.

- Define reinforcement. Compare and contrast positive and negative reinforcement. Interpret how conditioning explains adaptive behavior. Analyze the nature of primary and secondary reinforcers and superstitious behaviors.

- Describe the types of behavioral consequences that can act as punishers, explain how to use punishment effectively, and discuss the limitations.

- Explain how strength, timing, and frequency of consequences affect operant conditioning and how we can best utilize schedules of consequences in practical ways.

- Distinguish between stimulus generalization and stimulus discrimination in operant conditioning. Characterize extinction and spontaneous recovery as they relate to operant conditioning and human behavior.

- Explain how intrinsically and extrinsically motivated behaviors develop and what is meant by the hidden cost of reward.

- Explain the process of consolidation.

- Distinguish between insight, latent learning, and generative learning and describe how these concepts can be used to enhance our learning potential.

- Outline the eight cognitive techniques, described by McKeachie, used to create effective learning strategies and discuss how cooperative learning is leading to better methods of education.

- Describe how perceptual and cognitive influences are used in developing cognitive maps.

- State how observational learning theory suggests that people can learn new behaviors without being reinforced and explain the role of thought in establishing and maintaining these behaviors. List the key variables involved in observational learning.

# As you read...

## Pavlovian, or Classical , Conditioning Theory

1.      Define Learning.


2.      List the 3 important parts of learning.


3.      List 3 things internal to the organism that affect learning.


4.      Define Conditioning.


5.      What are a stimulus and a response?


6.      Define reflex.


7.      Reflexes and _____ _____ are both involuntary, but reflexes are not learned.


| 7-1      Terms and Procedures |
|---|

8.      Define classical or Pavlovian conditioning.


9.      What is an unconditioned stimulus and response?


10.      The stimulus that normally produces the response is called the _____ stimulus.


11.      What is a conditioned stimulus and response?


12.      The bell in Pavlov's experiment which caused the dogs to salivate as a result of learning was the _____ stimulus.

13.	The process of repeating trials to get the neutral stimulus to yield a conditioned response is called the _____ process.

---

**7-2	Classical Conditioning in Humans**

---

14.	Describe Marquis' classical conditioning of infants.

15.	Describe the conditioning of Albert.

16.	Identify the stimuli and responses that are involved in each of the following examples of classically conditioned behavior:

*unconditioned stimulus (UCS)	unconditioned response (UCR)*
*conditioned response (CR)	neutral stimulus that becomes the conditioned stimulus*
*(NS/CS)*

On several occasions Sybil's teacher gave her permission to draw on the blackboard. On each occasion, just as Sybil picked up the chalk, the recess bell that hung directly above where she was standing blasted a loud ring and startled her. Now whenever Sybil is asked to write on the blackboard, she feels apprehensive about having to touch the chalk.

UCS _____

UCR _____

NS/CS _____

CR _____

When Jake first adopted his pet cat, Tiger, he was able to use his electric can opener without any interference. However, after using the can opener many times just before giving Tiger his canned food, Jake finds that when he tries to use the appliance Tiger makes a nuisance of himself by standing underfoot and making anticipatory eating responses.

UCS _____

UCR _____

NS/CS _____

CR _____

**Higher Order Conditioning**

17. Define higher-order conditioning.

18. What 2 factors determine the extent of higher-order conditioning?

19. Give an example of higher order conditioning.

# Key Variables in Classical Conditioning

**7-4    Strength, Timing and Frequency**

1. Describe the importance of strength of the unconditioned stimulus.

2. How does the timing of the unconditioned stimulus impact conditioning?

3. How does the frequency of pairings impact conditioning?

**7-5    Predictability**

4. Define predictability.

5. The _____ of the association of the unconditioned and conditioned stimuli is key in determining whether conditioning will occur.

6. Predictability is considered a _____ _____ by many learning researchers.

**7-6    Extinction and Spontaneous Recovery**

7. Define extinction.

8. The process of withholding the unconditioned stimulus to reduce the probability of the conditioned response is called _____.

9. Psychologist say a behavior has been _____ when the conditioned stimulus no longer elicits the conditioned response.

10. Define spontaneous recovery.

---

| 7-7 | **Stimulus Generalization and Stimulus Discrimination** |

11. Define stimulus generalization.

12. The more _____ two stimuli are the more likely stimulus generalization is to occur.

13. What is stimulus discrimination?

14. What behaviors occur when it is difficult to discriminate between two stimuli?

---

| 7-8 | **Classical Conditioning in Daily Life** |

15. Describe the Garcia Effect.

16. The Garcia Effect is also referred to as _____ _____ _____.

17. Which two aspects of Garcia's research were surprising to learning researchers?

18. How does Bernstein's research deal with conditioned taste aversion in chemotherapy patients?

19. How does conditioning contribute to drug abuse?

20.    Can thoughts lead to conditioning?

21.    Identify the stimuli and responses that are involved in each of the following examples of classically conditioned behavior:

*unconditioned stimulus (UCS)*    *unconditioned response (UCR)*
*conditioned response (CR)*    *neutral stimulus that becomes the conditioned stimulus (NS/CS)*

Review item 16 and then create your own scenario for identifying the UCS< UCR< NS/CS, CR. Create the scenario from your own life experiences..

UCS _____

UCR _____

NS/CS _____

CR _____

# Operant Conditioning

**7-10    Pioneers: B. F. Skinner and E. L. Thorndike**

1.    How did Skinner view private events?

2.    B.F. Skinner wrote _____.

3.    Define operant conditioning.

4.    Operant conditioning is also known as _____.

5.    What are the key differences between classical and operant conditioning?

6.    Describe Thorndike's research with cats.
+

7. What are instrumental behaviors?

8. What is a reinforcer?

9. What is a punisher?

## 7-11 The Skinner Box and Shaping

10. What is a Skinner box?

11. Describe traditional operant conditioning.

12. Define shaping.

13. What is the method of successive approximations?

## 7-12 Reinforcement: A Consequence That Strengthens a Response

14. Define positive reinforcement.

15. Define negative reinforcement.

16. What is the difference between escape conditioning and avoidance conditioning?

17. A reinforcer that is based on the survival of an organism is called a
_____.

18. What is a secondary reinforcer?

19. What is superstitious behavior?

20.    Describe how electrical brain stimulation affects behaviors in rats.


| 7-13    Punishment: A Consequence that Weakens a Response |

21.    Define punishment.


22.    What are primary and secondary punishers?


23.    The combination of _____ of bad behaviors and _____ of desired behaviors is the most effective way to control behavior.


24.    What are the limitations of punishment?


25.    Describe learned helplessness.


|  | Desired stimulus | Noxious stimulus |
|---|---|---|
| Stimulus is presented after a particular behavior | Positive reinforcement | Punishment |
| Stimulus is removed after a particular behavior | Punishment | Negative reinforcement |

26.    In each of the four boxes in the table above, draw an arrow pointing either up (for increase) or down (for decrease) to indicate how the behavior will be affected by the consequence.


27.    Define the following types of punishment and punishers; give an example of each.

A) Punishment _____

   A.    Example _____

B) Removal of a pleasant stimulus _____

   A.    Example _____

C) Time-out _____

    A.    Example _____

D) Primary punisher _____

    A.    Example _____

E) Secondary punisher _____

    A.    Example _____

# Key Variables in Operant Conditioning

## 7-14    Strength, Timing and Frequency

1.    How does strength of consequences impact operant conditioning?

2.    The shorter the time interval between the _____ _____ and the _____ the greater the likelihood that the behavior will be learned.

3.    What is a schedule of reinforcement?

4.    Describe the following types of reinforcement schedules and tell what kind of response output can be expected from each.

    Fixed-interval _____

    Response output _____

    Variable interval _____

    Response output _____

    Fixed-ratio _____

    Response output _____

    Variable-ratio _____

    Response output _____

5.    Give the efficient combination of schedules to teach a response.

6.    What is one way to increase employee productivity?

7-15    **Stimulus Generalization and Stimulus Discrimination**

7.    How is stimulus generalization and discrimination different in operant conditioning?

8.    Define phobia.

9.    Describe systematic desensitization.

10.    Why does systematic desensitization work?

7-16    **Extinction and Spontaneous Recovery**

11.    Define extinction.

12.    How is extinction affected by the reinforcement schedule?

13.    How is spontaneous recovery in operant conditioning affected by the number of rest periods?

7-17    **Operant Conditioning in Daily Life**

14.    Define intrinsically motivated behaviors.

15.    Define extrinsically motivated behaviors.

16.    How does reinforcement affect intrinsically motivated behaviors?

17.    How do Behavioral regulation theorists view behavior?

18.     What 3 things must people do to regulate themselves?


# The Biology That Underpins Learning

## 7-18    Nature and Nurture

1.    Define nature.


2.    Define nurture.


3.    What is wildlife rehabilitation?


## 7-19    Is Evolutionary Theory Incompatible?

4.    What is evolutionary theory?


5.    Why is evolutionary theory not incompatible with learning theory?


## 7-20    Biological Codes

6.    What is a reverberating circuit?


7.    How does Hebb view learning and neurons?


8.    Define consolidation.


9.    What does animal research indicate about consolidation?


10.    How does repeated associations impact neurons?

# Cognitive Learning

1. Are there cognitive abilities different in men and women?

2. How are males and females taught to learn differently?

3. Differences are greater _____ women then _____ men and women.

| 7-21 | Insight |
|------|---------|

4. Define insight.

5. Describe Köhler's research with chimpanzees.

6. Insight requires no direct _____ or further training.

| 7-22 | Latent Learning |
|------|-----------------|

7. Define latent learning.

8. How do we know latent learning takes place?

9. What did Tolman propose about learning?

| 7-23 | Generative Learning |
|------|---------------------|

11. Define generative learning.

12. What is the generative learning model?

13. What does the generative learning model say about classroom learning?

## 7-24    Learning to Learn and Cooperative Learning

1.    List and describe the 8 cognitive techniques that can benefit students.

2.    Define metacognition.

3.    Define cooperative learning.

4.    What advantages are there to cooperative learning?

5.    What are the 7 myths that stunt people's learning growth?

## 7-25    Cognitive Maps

6.    Define cognitive maps.

7.    How does Allen say cognitive maps are formed?

8.    How do people learn routes?

## 7-26    Theories of Observational Learning

9.    Define observational learning theory.

10.    Observational learning theory is also referred to as _____ _____ _____.

11.    What are the key variables in observational learning?

12.    Identify the type of learning process that would be involved in establishing the italicized behaviors in each of the following situations.

|   *classical conditioning* | *operant conditioning* | *observational learning* |
|---|---|---|

A) _____ On several occasions during lightening storms, when Terry switched on the kitchen light she received a shock that caused severe pain. Now, even when the sky is clear, she feels *frightened as she touches the kitchen light switch.*

B) _____ Randy used an aerosol product to soothe his painful sunburn. The product eliminated the pain and now whenever Randy is sunburned, *he uses the product.*

C) _____ Lee's cat Belle purrs when its scalp is scratched. When Lee gets home from work she usually does two things in this sequence: she plays Beethoven's Ninth Symphony on her stereo, and she scratches Belle's head while she listens. One day Lee played the Ninth Symphony but she did not have time to scratch the cat's head. She noticed with surprise that when the music began, *Belle began to purr.*

D) _____ Daryl, who has never eaten a Chinese meal before, watched his friends eat for several minutes and then he too *positioned his chopsticks in his hand* and began to eat.

Learning
Conditioning
Reflex
Classical Conditioning
Unconditioned Stimulus
Unconditioned Response
Conditioned Stimulus
Conditioned Response
Higher-Order Conditioning
Extinction
Spontaneous Recovery
Stimulus Generalization
Stimulus Discrimination
Operant Conditioning
Skinner Box
Shaping
Reinforcer

Positive Reinforcement
Negative Reinforcement
Primary Reinforcer
Secondary Reinforcer
Superstitious Behavior
Punishment
Primary Punisher
Secondary Punisher
Learned Helplessness
Fixed-Interval Schedule
Variable-Interval Schedule
Fixed-Ratio Schedule
Variable-Ratio Schedule
Extinction
Latent Learning
Observational Learning Theory

# After you read . . . Self Test

## Chapter 7 Self Test

1. Psychologists define learning as: (222)
   A. a process that increases the intelligence and creativity of an individual.
   B. the acquisition of new knowledge.
   C. the ability to think rationally.
   D. a relatively permanent change in behavior that occurs as a result of experience.

2. Conditioning is defined in your text as: (235)
   A. modifying reflexive behavior.
   B. being prepared to respond to stimuli.
   C. being able to tell the difference between stimuli.
   D. a systematic procedure through which new responses to stimuli are learned.

3. Karen's father had several accidents while she was a passenger in his car. By the time she was eighteen, riding in a car as a passenger was so frightening for Karen that she could not go anywhere if someone else was going to drive. In this case, the unconditioned stimulus was: (224)
   A. the accidents.
   B. fear.
   C. the car.
   D. her father.

4. In Pavlov's classical conditioning experiment the _____ acted as an unconditioned stimulus. (225)
   A. food
   B. bell
   C. dog trainer
   D. salivation

5. Extinction is the term used to describe: (228-229)
   A. a process where the unconditioned stimulus is no longer paired with the conditioned stimulus.
   B. a conditioned response that is no longer elicited by the conditioned stimulus.
   C. a situation where the reinforcer is withheld.
   D. all of the above

6. Randy taps her foot and gets involved in the tune whenever she hears a country song. However, if the music is not country, she does not even know its playing. Randy's response to country music illustrates: (230)
   A. formation of a conditioned stimulus.
   B. instrumental conditioning.
   C. stimulus discrimination.
   D. stimulus generalization.

7. Whether or not conditioning takes place depends on the predictability of the association between the: (228)
   A.   NS and CS.
   B.   UCS and CS.
   C.   UCS and CR.
   D.   NS and UCR.

8. The Garcia effect is: (231-232)
   A.   organisms learning to avoid foods that make them sick.
   B.   pairing pills with nausea such that an aversion is produced in animals.
   C.   cancer patients avoiding certain foods following their chemotherapy.
   D.   all of the above

9. Psychologists call behavior that receives feedback in the form of a reinforcing or punishing consequence _____ behavior. (234)
   A.   respondent
   B.   classical
   C.   operant
   D.   involuntary

10. A device that allows researchers to control when an organism will receive reinforcement or punishment is called a: (235)
    A.   cumulative recorder.
    B.   Skinner box.
    C.   maze.
    D.   differential apparatus.

11. When lever pressing is being conditioned and we see the rat consistently turning its head prior to pressing the lever, we would say that superstitious behavior had occurred as a result of the head turn being: (238)
    A.   deliberately reinforced.
    B.   unintentionally reinforced.
    C.   placed on extinction.
    D.   tested for spontaneous recovery.

12. In order for a consequence to act as a reinforcer, the organism must: (237)
    A.   know that it has made the correct response.
    B.   feel positive about the response it has made.
    C.   understand the value of the consequence.
    D.   need or want the consequence.

13. If using punishment to discipline a particular behavior, a parent should: (240-241)
    A.   positively reinforce desired behaviors that are incompatible with the undesired behavior.
    B.   use a very mild punisher.
    C.   punish the behavior on a variable-interval schedule.
    D.   all of the above

14. Ratio schedules of consequences are based on: (244)
    A.    time passing between responses.
    B.    time passing between a response and a consequence.
    C.    the frequency of responses (i.e., work output).
    D.    the number of consequences that are given for one response.

15. On several occasions Julie found and bought her favorite dresses at Cecilia's Discount Clothing store. Now, whenever she does shopping for clothes, she heads for the nearest discount store. Julie's habit of shopping at any discount store illustrates: (246)
    A.    higher-order conditioning.
    B.    latent learning.
    C.    generalization.
    D.    discrimination.

16. When provided with hypothalamic stimulation, rats will: (239)
    A.    attach members of their own species.
    B.    fall asleep.
    C.    stop responding.
    D.    frequently choose brain stimulation over food.

17. A conditioned stimulus was repeatedly paired with an unconditioned stimulus. When the trainer presented the conditioned stimulus alone, the subject responded with a(an): (225)
    A.    unconditioned stimulus.
    B.    conditioned stimulus.
    C.    unconditioned response.
    D.    conditioned response.

18. According to Watson and Raynor, which of the following can human beings sometimes acquire through classical conditioning? (226)
    A.    intense disgust
    B.    parental instincts
    C.    strong fears
    D.    new skills

19. Antabuse is a drug that reacts with alcohol to cause nausea and vomiting. If Antabuse were used to treat alcoholism, this would be an application of: (231-232)
    A.    stimulus generalization.
    B.    conditioned taste aversions.
    C.    negative reinforcement.
    D.    higher-order conditioning.

20. A conditioned stimulus that has ceased to produce conditioned reactions is presented at a later time and again evokes those responses. This process is known as: (229)
    A.    spontaneous recovery.
    B.    acquisition.
    C.    stimulus generalization.
    D.    extinction.

21. Name the procedure in which subjects are given reinforcers for performing behaviors which get closer and closer to some target behavior. (236)
    A.    tracing
    B.    observational learning
    C.    shaping
    D.    flooding

22. Select an example of a primary reinforcer. (238)
    A.    books
    B.    food
    C.    money
    D.    praise

23. On which of the following schedules would a salesman be given a bonus for every fifth item sold? (244)
    A.    variable ratio
    B.    variable interval
    C.    fixed ratio
    D.    fixed interval

24. Which behaviors would be repeated for their own sake? (247-248)
    A.    latently learned
    B.    extrinsically motivated
    C.    secondary reinforced
    D.    intrinsically motivated

25. The Garcia taste-aversion effect is a type of classical conditioning that CONTRADICTS the traditional principle that (231)
    A.    understanding the situation is important for conditioning.
    B.    conditioning only works with very short time intervals.
    C.    stimuli must be paired over and over for conditioning.
    D.    conditioning has no real effect on important behaviors.

26. The presentation of a rewarding or pleasant stimulus after some behavior, to increase the likelihood of the behavior, is (237)
    A.    positive reinforcement.
    B.    negative reinforcement.
    C.    stimulus discrimination.
    D.    stimulus generalization.

27. Maritta bought her weekly lottery ticket at a different store than usual one week, and that was the week she won a respectable prize. She now prefers to buy her tickets at that store. This is an example of (238-239)
    A.    stimulus generalization.
    B.    superstitious behavior.
    C.    an unconditioned response.
    D.    a conditioned response.

28. Punishment can be administered in two ways: (239)
    A.   delivering a pleasant stimulus or removing an unpleasant stimulus.
    B.   delivering an unpleasant stimulus or removing a pleasant stimulus.
    C.   through classical conditioning or operant conditioning principles.
    D.   either before or after the behavior that is being conditioned.

29. A dental insurance company will reimburse claims for regular checkups only if at least six months have passed since the last checkup. This is an example of a _____ schedule of reinforcement. (243)
    A.   fixed ratio
    B.   variable ratio
    C.   fixed interval
    D.   variable interval

30. When an organism receives a reinforcer for correctly discriminating between two stimuli, it illustrates (246)
    A.   stimulus generalization.
    B.   stimulus discrimination.
    C.   classical conditioning.
    D.   primary reinforcement.

31. A hospital-based program for helping heart attack patients follow their new lifestyle requirements has the patients chart their own behaviors, observe their progress, and reward their achievements with rewards of their choice. This program uses principles of (249)
    A.   classical conditioning.
    B.   spontaneous recovery.
    C.   continuous reinforcement.
    D.   behavioral regulation.

32. Research by Bandura and others on how children respond to witnessing aggressive actions, for instance on TV, shows that watching aggression will make children act more aggressively (258)
    A.   in almost every case that was tested.
    B.   only under the most unusual conditions.
    C.   unless the observed aggressive person is punished.
    D.   if parents and teachers put too much emphasis on it.

33. In classical conditioning, the stimulus that is neutral prior to conditioning is referred to as _____. (225)
    A.   unconditioned stimulus
    B.   unconditioned response
    C.   conditioned stimulus
    D.   conditioned response

34. Pavlov's dogs were trained to salivate in response to a bell. After repeatedly pairing the bell with a light, the dogs begin to salivate in response to the light. This is an example of: (226)
    A.   extinction
    B.   higher-order conditioning
    C.   stimulus generalization
    D.   acquisition process

35. Classical conditioning occurs more easily if: (227)
    A.   the unconditioned stimulus is strong.
    B.   there is a long delay between the presentation of the unconditioned stimulus and the neutral stimulus.
    C.   the unconditioned stimulus and the neutral stimulus are rarely paired together.
    D.   the neutral stimulus can not be predicted by the unconditioned stimulus.

36. When the conditioned stimulus is repeatedly presented without the unconditioned stimulus, in order to reduce the probability of the conditioned response occurring, it is called: (228-229)
    A.   spontaneous recovery
    B.   operant conditioning
    C.   extinction
    D.   stimulus discrimination

37. The Richardsons are trying to get their son to study more. To try to get their son to study more, they give him money for every test that he does well on in school. This is an example of: (237)
    A.   positive reinforcement
    B.   negative reinforcement
    C.   positive punishment
    D.   negative punishment

38. Punishment and negative reinforcement are (239)
    A.   different terms for the same concept
    B.   different in terms of their effect on behavior
    C.   same because both reduce behaviors
    D.   same because both increase emotions

39. Which is an example of a secondary reinforcer? (238)
    A.   food
    B.   praise
    C.   termination of pain
    D.   spanking

40. A rat is being trained to pressing a lever. The rat is given a food pellet after pressing the lever five times. The rat is on a _____ schedule of reinforcement. (244)
    A.   Fixed interval
    B.   Variable interval
    C.   Fixed ratio
    D.   Variable ratio

41. Research on schedules of reinforcement suggest that when reinforcement is linked to _____ people work harder to achieve. (245)
    A.   interval
    B.   time
    C.   output
    D.   frequency

42. A fitness program which requires the participants to chart their own nutrition, exercise and aerobic activity is using the principles of (249)
    A.   self stimulation
    B.   negative reinforcement
    C.   observational learning
    D.   behavioral self regulation

43. The idea that learning occurs in the absence of direct reinforcement and is not necessarily demonstrated through observable behavior is called: (254)
    A.   generative learning
    B.   insight
    C.   cooperative learning
    D.   latent learning

44. Which is not an element of observational learning? (259)
    A.   the power of the model
    B.   the independence of the learner
    C.   the personality of the learner
    D.   the appearance of the learner

45. The model that suggest people learn as a result of the learner generating meaning between past experiences and the present is called (254)
    A.   latent learning
    B.   generative learning
    C.   insight
    D.   cooperative learning

# When You Have Finished

## Essay Questions:

1. Describe classical conditioning with allergies and the immune system. (232-233)

2. Describe the difference between negative reinforcement and punishment. (239-240)

3. Describe how neurons are affected by learning. (251)

4. Describe how imitation and punishment can interact and the consequences. (241)

5. Describe the process of avoidance conditioning and how it can explain both adaptive behaviors and irrational fears. (237)

# Chapter 8

# Memory

## Before you read...

Chapter 8 begins with a description of memory in terms of the information-processing approach and looks at the process involved in memory and outlines three stages of memory: encoding, storage, and retrieval. The levels of processing approach breaks from the linear model suggested by the information processing approach and states that memory is processed at varying levels or depths depending on the cues provided. The neuroscience approach refers to the electrochemical process and proposes that memories are stored in multiple locations throughout the nervous system.

Memory is divided into sensory memory, short-term memory, and long-term memory. Sensory memory focuses on the encoding process and is temporary and fragile. Short-term memory focuses on storage. Memories can be stored for longer periods of time if techniques like rehearsal are used. Long-term memory focuses on the retrieval process and is thought to have a limitless capacity. Two types of information can be stored in long-term memory, including procedural and declarative. Declarative memory is further divided into episodic and semantic memory, episodic memory being based on the chronological sequence of events, objects, or situations, and semantic memory on memory for ideas, rules, and general concepts. Consolidation theory supports the neuroscience approach to memory by postulating that memories are processed and later distributed to thousands of neurons in the brain. This biochemical approach may hold the key to a better understanding of how and why we remember or forget..

The process of retrieval has generated hundreds of research studies, most of which focus on the accuracy of recall and methods to improve recall. Lefton discusses primacy and recency effects, imagery techniques, and extraordinary memory, and provides some practical suggestions for improving your memory. Memory for distinctive events is termed <u>flashbulb memory</u>

Forgetting can be caused by a number of factors including improper rehearsal or not using memory for an extended period. To prevent forgetting information, one must develop an understanding of how information is retrieved. Specific measures of retention are described, including recall and recognition. Each of these measures helps explain how we remember or forget information. Decay and interference can cause forgetting, and information can be lost from both short- and long-term memory. Although some suggest that memories are retained, but sometimes not readily available, this usually is due to improper encoding or some other secondary cause. Lefton examines memory in the context of state-dependent learning, motivated forgetting and eyewitness testimony.

Amnesia is the inability to remember information because of some physiological trauma. Retrograde amnesia is the inability to remember events that preceded the trauma, and anterograde amnesia is the inability to remember events following the trauma. .

It may never be clear where remembering ends and forgetting starts, but if you use your knowledge of memory, you will begin to enhance your own memories.

# Chapter Objectives

- Detail how encoding, storage, and retrieval are involved in memory processes.

- Describe the levels of processing approach and the neuroscience approach to memory.

- Describe the two types of encoding that take place in sensory memory.

- Describe how short-term memory differs from sensory memory by actively processing information and using different types of rehearsal. Also, discuss how duration and capacity limitations in short term memory.

- Describe the encoding and storage processes characteristic of long-term memory; also make distinctions between procedural and declarative memory.

- Explain how the consolidation process may explain both memory and learning. State what is known about the location of memories.

- Compare and contrast episodic with semantic memory and explicit with implicit memory.

- Examine the phenomenon of state-dependent learning.

- Interpret the practicality of an understanding of primacy and recency effects and how imagery can be used as an important perceptual memory aid.

- Discuss the research findings of early memory studies concerning relearning, and the *von Restorff* effect.

- Discuss recall, recognition, and reconstruction as measures of retention and describe their relationship to schema.

- Describe how memory is lost through decay and interference and differentiate between proactive interference, retroactive interference, and interference in attention.

- Examine the contradictory research findings concerning the accuracy of eyewitness testimony.

- Examine the debate between clinical psychologists and memory researchers on the issue of motivated forgetting.

- Distinguish between anterograde and retrograde amnesia

# As you read...

## Memory: The Brain as Information Processor

1. Define memory.


2. Define information processing.


3. What is encoding?


4. The second process of memory is _____.


5. Define retrieval.


# Encoding

1.   Define attention.


2.   What is the role of attention in encoding?


3.   Define metacognition.


| 8-1 | Levels of Processing |
|-----|----------------------|

4.   Define the levels of processing approach.


5.   The more complex the level of processing the _____ the code goes into memory.


6.   Describe the encoding specificity principle?


7.   What is transfer-appropriate processing?

8. The process of encoding is affected by both the demands of _____ and the _____ provided.

9. Describe confirmation bias and give an example.

| 8-2 | **Neuroscience and Encoding** |

10. According to Tulving's research how are the left and right prefrontal cortexes involved in memory?

11. What has fMRI research shown about the temporal lobes in encoding and retrieval?

12. _____ _____ show different brain activation during encoding are retrieval tasks.

# Storage

1. What are memory stores?

2. Describe the 3 stage model for memory storage.

| 8-3 | **Sensory Memory** |

3. Define sensory memory.

4. Sensory memory is sometimes referred to as the _____ _____.

5. What does Sperling's research show about the capacity of sensory memory?

6. What is an icon?

7. Describe iconic storage.

8.      What is the storage mechanism for the auditory system?

| 8-4 | **Short-Term Storage** |

9.      Define short-term memory.


10.     Define working memory.


11.     How are short-term storage and working memory different?


12.     What is the memory span?


13.     Define chunks.


14.     What is rehearsal?


15.     Describe the 2 types of rehearsal.


16.     New information may _____ with the recall of other information in working memory.


17.     What is the visual-spatial scratchpad or blackboard?


18.     What is the function of the executive in working memory?

| 8-5 | **Long-Term Memory** |

19.     Define long-term memory.


20.     What is the capacity of long-term memory?

21. Define procedural memory.

22. The necessary memory to operate a car, wash dishes, or swim involves
_____ memory.

23. What is declarative memory?

24. Describe episodic memory.

25. One particular type of episodic memory _____ _____, is
comprised of memories about ourselves.

26. Define semantic memory.

27. What is explicit memory?

28. Describe implicit memory.

29. How does practice affect storage?

| 8-6 | **Neuroscience and Storage** |
|---|---|

30. Describe the different areas of the brain that become active during different working
memory tasks.

31. What problems did H.M. have with memory?

32. As a result of the research with H.M., researchers began looking at the
_____ and its role in memory.

33. Define consolidation.

34.    What is long-term potentiation?

35.    Where is long-term memory stored in the brain?

36.    What type of memory is most affected with age?

37.    What are neurofibrillary tangles?

38.    Define plaque.

39.    Describe the types and progression of memory loss in Alzheimer's patients.


# Retrieval

| 8-7 | Retention: Measures of Retrieval |
|---|---|

1.    Define retrieval.

2.    Define retention.

3.    What is recall?

4.    Describe the 3 types of recall tasks.

5.    Describe recognition tasks.

6.    Define relearning.


| 8-8 | Retrieval Success and Failure: Encoding Specificity |
|---|---|

7.    Forgotten information is not gone, just _____.

8.      Describe the encoding specificity principal.

9.      Describe Bahrick's research.

10.     What is an ex post facto study?

11.     What is a subject variable?

12.     Define state-dependant learning.

13.     Give an explanation for state-dependant learning.

## 8-9      Flashbulb Memory

14.     Define flashbulb memory.

15.     What is consequentiality?

16.     Are flashbulb memories more accurate than other memories?

17.     How are flashbulb memories created?

## 8-10     Gender and Memory

18.     Are there gender differences in recall?

19.     Gender differences in memory are the result of differences in _____.

20.     Describe how memory differences can be manipulated.

21.    What is the primacy effect?

22.    Words at the end of a list are easily recalled.  This is explained in the _____ effect phenomenon.

23.    Describe and draw a serial position curve.

24.    What is the von Restorff effect?

25.    Define imagery.

26.    How is imagery used as a memory aid?

# Forgetting: When Memory Fails

**8-12    Early Studies**

1.    Describe Ebbinghaus' research on forgetting.

2.    What is the saving method?

3.    Describe Bartlett's research on forgetting.

4.    List and describe the 3 changes people make to information they are trying to remember.

5.    Define schema.

## 8-13 Key Causes of Forgetting

6. Describe decay of information.

7. What is a memory trace?

8. Define interference.

9. Define and distinguish between proactive and retroactive interference.

10. _____ is due to interference in attention and is an encoding problem.

11. How does divided attention affect encoding and retrieval?

12. Describe the Stroop effect.

## 8-14 Special Types of Forgetting

13. What is eyewitness testimony?

14. Is eyewitness testimony infallible?

15. What can investigators do to improve the accuracy of eyewitness testimony?

16. Describe the misinformation effect.

17. What is memory enhancement?

18. Describe motivated forgetting.

19.    What 3 questions must be answered to solve the debate over the accuracy of recovered memories?


20.    What does research say about the answers to these questions?


21.    How can false memories be created?


| 8-15   Neuroscience and Forgetting |
| --- |


22.    Define amnesia.


23.    Identify the concept that explains why remembering or forgetting occurs in each of the following situations.

*decay*                          *retrograde amnesia*
*retroactive inhibition*         *anterograde amnesia*
*proactive inhibition*           *primacy effect*
*motivated forgetting*           *recency effect*

A) _____ Joyce could not remember her grandfather's version of the family's traditional Thanksgiving blessing after having recited a different one at a church social gathering.

B) _____ When Sam arrived at the company party he was introduced to twelve other guests. Sam can remember the names of the first three people he met.

C) _____ As a result of a serious head injury Jennifer suffered some brain damage. She remembers things like her name, where she grew up, and what she was doing before the accident. However, she cannot remember who her doctor is, what she ate for breakfast, or that her mother visited her yesterday.

D) _____ For years, as a child, Dale dialed his friend Leon's phone number from memory. Ten years later while visiting his hometown, Dale decided to phone Leon's parents to see if they could help him get in touch with his old friend. When Dale went to dial the number he realized that he could not remember it.

E) _____ Doug studied his psychology vocabulary words and then his sociology vocabulary words. His accuracy in recalling the sociology vocabulary words was poor.

F) _____ Somehow Claire lost her grocery list on the way to the store. Although she had read over the list just before leaving home, when she began to shop she realized that all she could remember were the last few items on the list.

G) _____ When David was five years old he lost his puppy, which upset him very much. When his mother related the story later she said she thought it strange that he did not remember the event, because the puppy had been so important to him and the loss was so traumatic. David's mother suggested that perhaps he did not want to remember.

H) _____ While climbing a mountain Frank fell and received a serious blow to his head. When he regained consciousness, he did not know who he was, where he came from, or when he was born.

**Term Identification: Make flashcards for each of the following terms. Hint: Use the definitions in the margins of the chapter**

Memory
Encoding
Levels-of-Processing Approach
Encoding Specificity Principle
Transfer-Appropriate Processing
Storage
Sensory Memory
Memory Span
Chunks
Rehearsal
Maintenance Rehearsal
Elaborative Rehearsal
Short-Term Memory
Working Memory
Long-Term Memory
Procedural Memory
Declarative Memory
Episodic Memory

Semantic Memory
Explicit Memory
Implicit Memory
Consolidation
Retrieval
State-Dependent Learning
Primacy Effect
Recency Effect
Imagery
Schema
Decay
Interference
Proactive Interference
Retroactive Interference
Amnesia
Retrograde Amnesia
Anterograde Amnesia

# After you read . . . Self Test

## Chapter 8 Self Test

1.  Even though something is learned it may not always be remembered because: (264)
    A.    learning is a relatively permanent change.
    B.    learning and memory are two separate processes.
    C.    memory is the ability to remember past events, information, or skills.
    D.    A and C

2.  _____ refers to the process of directing mental effort to some features of the environment and not to others (265)
    A.    recall
    B.    storage
    C.    encoding
    D.    attention

3.  The sensory register provides: (269)
    A.    coding and storage for about 30 seconds
    B.    coding and permanent storage.
    C.    initial encoding of information and brief, temporary storage.
    D.    encoding, storage, and retrieval.

4.  A chunk: (271)
    A.    can be a letter, a group of words and numbers, or sentences organized in a familiar way.
    B.    is a manageable and meaningful unit of information.
    C.    a brief and limited number of items that can be easily reproduced after presentation.
    D.    A and B

5.  Procedural memory: (274)
    A.    is memory for specific facts.
    B.    is storage for the perceptual, motor, and cognitive skills necessary to complete a task.
    C.    covers specific events, objects, and situations.
    D.    covers the memory of ideas, rules, and general concepts about the world.

6.  Recall of words at the end of a list is an example of: (283)
    A.    recency effect.
    B.    extraordinary memory.
    C.    primacy effect.
    D.    rehearsal of information.

7. _____ involves the organization of sensory information so that the nervous system can process it. (265)
   A. storage
   B. recall
   C. attention
   D. encoding

8. Paivio and other researchers argue that imagery, verbal coding mechanisms, and semantic memory operate together to: (285)
   A. code information.
   B. retrieve information.
   C. form conceptual memory.
   D. both A and B

9. An example of state dependent learning would be: (280-281)
   A. learning information while sober and recalling while intoxicated.
   B. learning and recalling information while sober.
   C. the tendency to recall information learned in a particular psychological state more accurately when one is again in that psychological state.
   D. learning information while intoxicated and recalling while sober.

10. According to the levels of processing theory, when the level of processing becomes more complex, a memory code _____. (266)
    A. will be more deeply incorporated into memory stores
    B. is likely to suffer from retrograde forgetting
    C. will not be encoded into memory stores
    D. is easily forgotten because it is too difficult

11. Relearning a skill or information easily is an example of: (286)
    A. recall.
    B. retrieval.
    C. saving method.
    D. retention.

12. Contemporary explanations of reconstructive memory have focused on: (286-287)
    A. schema.
    B. leveling.
    C. sharpening.
    D. assimilation.

13. The decay hypothesis is not as widely accepted today, because many early studies did not take into consideration variables such as: (288)
    A. interference and crowding.
    B. proactive and retroactive inhibition.
    C. rate and mode of stimulus presentation.
    D. coding and chunking.

14. Retroactive inhibition is: (288)
    A.    retrieval failure.
    B.    the decrease in accurate recall of an item as a result of later presentation of other items.
    C.    the increase in accurate recall of an item as a result of later presentation of other items.
    D.    the decrease in accurate recall as a result of previous events interfering with a to-be remembered one.

15. Burying unpleasant ideas in the unconscious where they remain inaccessible is an example of: (293)
    A.    motivated forgetting.
    B.    amnesia.
    C.    retrograde amnesia.
    D.    anterograde amnesia.

16. The hippocampus region of the brain is responsible for: (276)
    A.    remembering old information, but not new information.
    B.    the ability to remember remote events.
    C.    the transfer of new information to permanent memory.
    D.    the ability to remember new information, but not old information.

17. To aid in the retrieval of information, research regarding the _____ suggests that you should study the same way you will be tested. That is, if you will be tested using an essay format, you should study by developing essay answered to possible questions. (267)
    A.    parallel distributed process
    B.    encoding specificity principle
    C.    metacognitive appeal principle
    D.    transfer-appropriate processing principle

18. When one is unable to accesses memories only seconds after exposure, it can be said that these _____ never made it into _____. (268)
    A.    flashbulb memories; long-term storage
    B.    flashbulb memories; short-term storage
    C.    sensory memories; long-term storage
    D.    sensory memories; short-term storage

19. Hebb argues that _____ serves as the basis of short-term memory and permits _____ of information into long-term memory. (276)
    A.    coding, consolidation
    B.    consolidation, coding
    C.    neural activity, circuits
    D.    circuits, neural activity

20. Information can be held in short-term memory for about _____. (271)
    A.    2-3 minutes
    B.    1- 11/2 minutes
    C.    20-30 seconds
    D.    5-10 seconds

21. _____ memory is the memory store for specific events or facts (274)
    A.    declarative
    B.    restorative
    C.    procedural
    D.    consolidated

22. Your grandmother tells you detailed stories from her childhood.  She is relating information that is stored in her _____ memory (274)
    A.    procedural
    B.    sensory
    C.    episodic
    D.    semantic

23. Implicit memory tasks indirectly test: (275)
    A.    knowledge acquired through study
    B.    unconsciously remembered knowledge
    C.    emotional memory traces
    D.    a person's personal retrieval strategies

24. Even though it is years since Phil witnessed a fatal auto accident, he still remembers every detail very vividly. This is an example of a(n) (281-282)
    A.    implicit memory
    B.    procedural memory
    C.    semantic memory
    D.    flashbulb memory

25. How is information retained in memory? (268)
    A.    storage
    B.    reminiscence
    C.    retrieval
    D.    encoding

26. What is the storage mechanism for visual sensory memory called? (269)
    A.    mantra storage
    B.    echoic storage
    C.    iconic storage
    D.    none of the above

27. When studying for a test, you may learn definitions by repeating them over and over.  This process is known as: (271)
    A.    consolidation.
    B.    indexing.
    C.    rehearsal.
    D.    categorization.

28. The best way to remember new material for a long time is to: (271)
    A. relate it to information already in the long-term memory.
    B. repeat it to yourself several times.
    C. play a tape of the information while you are sleeping.
    D. use rote memory.

29. What type of memory stores the ability to type? (274)
    A. declarative
    B. procedural
    C. representational
    D. propositiona

30. Jeff could only remember the names of the last two people he met at the reception. This is an example of: (283)
    A. the recency effect.
    B. chunking.
    C. the initialization principle.
    D. the primacy effect.

31. Explicit memory tasks usually require subjects to: (275)
    A. use creative strategies to solve problems
    B. perform complex tasks without the benefit of direct instructions
    C. use recall and recognition strategies to identify information that is not deliberately learned
    D. use recall and recognition strategies to identify previously studied material

32. Which of the following is required when material must be recalled in a specific order? (278)
    A. structured recall
    B. serial recall
    C. fixed recall
    D. free recall

33. Name the two types of amnesia. (294)
    A. physiological and psychological
    B. retrograde and anterograde
    C. temporary and permanent
    D. cortical and hippocampal

34. _____ is a suggested cause of forgetting involving the suppression of one bit of information by another received earlier or later of the confusion of two pieces of information. (288)
    A. interference
    B. decay
    C. representation
    D. memory tracing

35. Hans was in an auto accident, and for a long time he couldn't remember anything that happened for a day or two leading up to the accident. This is an example of (294)
    A. anterograde amnesia
    B. retrograde amnesia
    C. proactive interference
    D. retroactive interferece

36. Which type of memory can be described as lasting only for a brief period of time and as the place where initial encoding occurs. (269)
    A. sensory
    B. short-term memory
    C. working memory
    D. long-term memory

37. Your ability to do well on these exam questions relies on: (274)
    A. short-term memory
    B. maintenance memory
    C. semantic memory
    D. episodic memory

38. When material can be remembered in any order, _____ it is called (278)
    A. serial recall
    B. free recall
    C. fixed recall
    D. recognition

39. People who suffer from anterograde amnesia will have the most difficulty remembering (294)
    A. something they think very hard about
    B. something that produces strong emotions
    C. something that happened many years ago
    D. something that happened an hour ago

40. The information-processing approach to the study of memory assumes that (264-265)
    A. memories are neither altered nor lost after they are stored in long-term memory
    B. there are separate stages in memory
    C. specific areas of the brain store specific types of information
    D. recognition and recall memory are served by different but related systems

41. Visual information can be held in sensory for about _____ while auditory information can be held for about _____. (269)
    A. 20-30 second; 3 seconds
    B. 250 milliseconds; 20-30 seconds
    C. 250 milliseconds; 3 seconds
    D. 3 seconds; 250 milliseconds

42. The function of the "central processing mechanism" in Baddeley's conception of working memory is most accurately described as (272)
    A.  monitoring the content of the sensory registers
    B.  seeing that information does not get lost or disgarded
    C.  retaining information by maintenance rehearsal
    D.  controlling the flow and processing of information

43. _____ is the process by which stored information is recovered from memory (278)
    A.  encoding
    B.  retrieval
    C.  storage
    D.  declaration

44. Subjects remember items they memorize at the beginning of a list better than they do items in the middle of the list illustrates the _____ (283)
    A.  massed practice effect
    B.  motivated forgetting
    C.  primacy effect
    D.  recency effect

45. Janet sees Carol frequently on campus and speaks to her. When she saw Carol in the department store, she couldn't remember her name. Her forgetting the name is best explained by (266)
    A.  the decay theory of forgetting
    B.  state-dependant learning theory
    C.  the encoding specificity hypothesis
    D.  Freud's idea of motivated forgetting

# When You Have Finished

## Essay Questions:

1. What parts of the brain are involved in forming long-term memory storage, where are these memories stored after being formed and what parts of the brain are activated during retrieval? (276-277)

2. Define the types of long-term memory, declarative, procedural, episodic and semantic.(274-275)

3. Describe the types of rehearsal and practice and how they improve memory. (271)

4. Describe the research on practice by Baddeley and Longman and what it indicates about the impact of the timing of practice (275)

5. What are false memories and how are they created? (293)

# Chapter 9

# Cognitive Psychology

# Before you read...

The chapters on consciousness, learning, and memory were concerned with how we attend to, acquire, store, and retrieve information. In Chapter 9 Lefton and Brannon blend the previous concepts into the application of thought and language. Cognitive psychologists are interested in a variety of thought-oriented issues, and many overlap other topics in psychology. In this chapter, the focus is on concept formation, problem solving, decision making, and language.

People organize their world by organizing their thoughts into concepts. Concept formation is thought to be the structure behind how each of us makes sense of the world. Concept formation is relatively easy to study in the laboratory; the two most common methods are the reception and selection methods. Each derives the formation of concepts, but the selection method is less structured. The problem with concept formation is that many concepts are termed <u>fuzzy concepts</u>, so that operational definitions are difficult.

Cognitive psychologists are interested in the thinking process. Lefton and Brannon examine in detail, syllogisms, logical decision making, and estimating probabilities. Problem solving is considered one of the highest cognitive processes. However, problem solving can be hindered by obstacles such as functional fixedness and mental set. Both can limit the available responses to problems. Critical thinking and creative problem solving are ways to expand on the possible solutions to problems. Lefton and Brannon suggest some ways to improve your problem solving skills. Computers also have the ability to problem solve by the use of algorithms and heuristics. Although computers can be programmed to simulate human problem solving, they lack (for now) ingenuity and imagination. Researchers are developing artificial neural networks which are interconnected units that serve as neural models. These models may someday answer many of the unanswered questions about human information processing.

People come from diverse cultures and experience life in many different contexts, but in all societies we have language. The study of psycholinguistics and the major areas of phonology (the study of the sounds of language), semantics (the study of the meaning of language), and syntax (the study of the relationships of words) are examined. Lefton and Brannon conclude this chapter with the nature versus nurture debate of language acquisition. Learning theorists contend that language is acquired through imitation and reinforcement, and biologists contend that humans are born with an innate predisposition. Chimpanzee studies are presented to critically evaluate these arguments.

# Chapter Objectives

- Describe the field of cognitive psychology and the cognitive processes studied by researchers.

- Assess the elements involved in concept formation and the methods researchers use to study it.

- Explain how psychologists can help people become better problem solvers. To gain a better understanding, focus on heuristics and algorithms.

- Examine how functional fixedness and metal set can interfere with problem-solving abilities.

- List the important attributes and stages of creative thought and distinguish between convergent and divergent thinking.

- Distinguish between the terms *reasoning* and *decision making* and develop an understanding of how logic is involved in each.

- Examine what psychological factors are involved in estimations of the probability of specific behaviors and events.

- Improve your decision-making skills by examining the stumbling blocks outlined as barriers.

- Explain how psychologists use computer simulations to mimic human information processing

- Expand your understanding of cognitive processes by examining the concept of neural networks

- Discuss how thoughts and culture influence language.

- Distinguish between linguistics and psycholinguistics and relate each of these areas of study to the acquisition of language.

- Describe what is learned through research in phonology, semantics, and syntax.

- Differentiate between learning and biological theories of language acquisition, especially as they relate to learning readiness.

- Discuss the research on language acquisition in chimpanzees, and explain how chimp language differs from human language.

# As you read...

## Cognitive Psychology: An Overview

1.    Define Cognitive Psychology.

## Concept Formation: the Process of Forming Mental Groups

1.    Define Concepts.

2.    What is an exemplar?

3.    What is the study of concept formation?

4.    The process of organizing things into categories is _____.

5.    Describe the basic design of laboratory studies in concept formation.

6.    What are positive and negative instances?

7.    Define prototype.

## Problem Solving: Confronting Situations that Require Solutions

1.    Define problem solving.

2.    What is an algorithm?

3.    What is a heuristic?

4.    Describe the 3 main heuristic approaches.

5.      Describe functional fixedness.


6.      Define mental set.


7.      When one experiences the inability to see another use for a familiar object, they are experiencing _____   _____.


8.      List and describe the 6 tips to make you a better critical thinker.


9.      Are you using any of the strategies already?


9-2      **Creative Problem Solving**

10.      Describe creativity.


11.      What are original, novel and appropriate responses?


12.      Compare and contrast convergent and divergent thinking.


13      In order to _____ all possible solutions must be considered without any initial judgments of worth.


14.      What are Sternberg's 6 interactive resources of problem solving?


15.      What is the investment theory of creativity?


# Reasoning and Decision Making

16.      Define reasoning.

16. _____ is a system of reasoning used to make inferences and reach valid conclusions.

17.    Describe decision making.


## 9-3    Uncertainty: Estimating Probabilities

18.    What is an educated guess?


19.    Define probability.


20.    _____ and _____ are especially useful for teaching students scientific concepts.


## 9-4    Barriers to Sound Decision Making

21.    What is the gambler's fallacy?


22.    How does belief in small numbers contribute to poor decision making?


23.    Define availability heuristic.


24.    Describe overconfidence and confirmation bias and how they lead to poor decisions.


## 9-5    Culture and Reasoning

25.    How do Chinese and European Americans differ in finding solutions to contradictory statements?


26.    How are these differences affected by the different traditions of these cultures?

| 9-6 | **Evolution and Reasoning** |

27.    How do the evolutionary psychologists view cognition?

28.    What type of logic problems are easier?

29.    Why do evolutionary psychologists think cognitive psychology has ignored important research areas?

# Artificial Intelligence

| 9-7 | **The Computer as Information Processor** |

30.    Define artificial intelligence.

31.    Why do researchers use the game of chess to study artificial intelligence?

32.    How do computers operate differently than humans?

| 9-8 | **Neural Networks** |

33.    Define convergence zone.

34.    What is blindsight?

35.    Define parallel distributed processing.

36.    What are artificial neural network?

# Language

1.    Define language.

2.     What does human language allow us to do that no animals can?

---

| 9-9 | **Language and Gender Stereotypes** |
|---|---|

3.     How are men and woman normally described differently?

4.     Research has shown that differences exist in men's and women's _____.

5.     Define androgyny.

---

| 9-10 | **Thought, Culture, and Language** |
|---|---|

6.     Language may _____ thought but language does not _____ thought.

7.     How does culture and language affect a person's responses to questions?

8.     Give 3 functions and the brain areas PET and fMRI research have shown to be active during those functions.

9.     What is the sylvian fissure thought to be responsible for?

10.    Is the brain hardwired for cognitive activities?

---

| 9-11 | **Linguistics** |
|---|---|

11.    Define linguistics.

12.    What is psycholinguistics?

13.    What is ASL?

14.    What are linguistic structures?

9-12    **Language Structure**

15.    List and describe the 3 major areas of psycholinguistic study.

16.    _____ are the basic units of sound that make up words.

17.    Different from the basic units of sound, _____ are the basic units of meaning in a language.

18.    What are semantics?

19.    Define telegraphese.

20.    The way groups of words come together to form language is called _____.

21.    The function of a language is called _____.

22.    Match the following terms with the appropriate definition.

| psycholinguistics | syntax |
|---|---|
| grammar | phonemes |
| phonology | morpheme |
| semantics | |

A) _____ The study of the basic units of sound found in a language.

B) _____ The basic unit of meaning in a language; a word or meaningful part of a word.

C) _____ The basic units of sound in a language.

D) _____ The study of how language is acquired, perceived, understood, and produced.

E) _____ The linguistic description of how a language functions.

F) _____ The relation between groups of words and how those words are arranged in phrases and sentences.

G) _____ The study of meanings of words and sentences, and the analysis of how thought is generated by the placement of words in a particular context.

| 9-13 | The Biological and Evolutionary Basis of Language |

23. What did Noam Chomsky suggest about language?

24. What research supports this idea?

# Language Acquisition

1. Describe Brown's research.

2. What is naturalistic observation?

3. What conclusions about language can be drawn from Brown's research?

| 9-14 | Learning Theories |

4. Describe the learning approach to language acquisistion.

5. What is a cochlear implant?

6. Why is their controversy about cochlear implants?

| 9-15 | Biological Theories |

7. What is LAD?

8.     List and describe the 3 types of evidence that support the nature side of nature vs nurture in language.


9.     Define lateralization.


| 9-16 | Language Studies with Chimpanzees |
| --- | --- |

10.     Describe the language of Washoe, Sarah, Lana and Nim.


11.     How is language different with chimpanzees than with humans?


| 9-17 | And What About Dolphins? |
| --- | --- |

12.     What did Janik's research show about dolphins?


13.     What does Miller and Bain's research indicate about whales and language?


14.     Do dolphins and whales have language?


| 9-18 | Social Interaction Theories: A Little Bit of Each |
| --- | --- |

15.     How is language both innate and reinforced?


16.     How does context affect language?


17.     What are the keys to understanding language acquisition?

**Term Identification: Make flashcards for each of the following terms. Hint: Use the definitions in the margins of the chapter**

Cognitive Psychology
Concept
Prototype
Problem Solving
Algorithm
Heuristics
Subgoal Analysis
Means-Ends Analysis
Backward Search
Functional Fixedness
Creativity
Convergent Thinking
Divergent Thinking
Brainstorming

Reasoning
Logic
Decision Making
Language
Linguistics
Psycholinguistics
Phonology
Phoneme
Morpheme
Semantics
Syntax
Grammar
Naturalistic Observation

# After you read . . . Self Test

## Chapter 9 Self Test

1.  The study of how we acquire, transform, store, retrieve and use knowledge is (300)
    A.  classical conditioning
    B.  cognitive psychology
    C.  intelligence testing
    D.  generativity

2.  A mental category of objects or events that are grouped together because they have some common properties is a(n) (301)
    A.  image
    B.  heuristic
    C.  mental set
    D.  concept

3.  If a child is shown examples from a set of figures (triangle, square, and circle) that are large, middle-sized and small, and told that the large square is an example of the concept, the experimenter is using _____ of the concept (302)
    A.  a positive instance
    B.  a negative instance
    C.  a discriminant
    D.  the rule

4.  Errors in probability judgments may be attributed to: (308-309)
    A.  ethical systems or religious beliefs.
    B.  ignoring key pieces of data.
    C.  an individual's political view.
    D.  all of the above

5.  Functional fixedness increases when: (305)
    A.  an object has no name or label to describe it.
    B.  an object has no specific function.
    C.  a person has had previous experience with an object.
    D.  all of the above

6.  Brainstorming: (307)
    A.  decreases functional fixedness.
    B.  promotes creativity.
    C.  produces a higher quality of ideas.
    D.  all of the above

7. Computers have been programmed to simulate human thought processes like: (312)
   A. information processing.
   B. ingenuity.
   C. creativity.
   D. A & C

8. A prototype of a concept is a member of the concept that (302)
   A. specifies exactly what members must be like
   B. is one of the best examples of the concept
   C. gives correct and incorrect properties of the concept
   D. applies to artificial concepts, but not fuzzy concepts

9. Language and thought are: (316-317)
   A. related, but separate processes.
   B. both influenced by one's experience with the environment.
   C. both influenced by genetic factors.
   D. all of the above

10. Suppose this weekend you have to take your clothes to the laundry, because everything you own is dirty, but you also want to see a movie, and you don't have enough money to do both. In the terminology of a cognitive psychology, your ability to figure out what to do will depend on your capacity for (303)
    A. hypothesis testing
    B. problem solving
    C. syllogistic reasoning
    D. linguistic determinism

11. A phoneme is the basic unit of _____ in a language. (319)
    A. sound
    B. meaning
    C. inflection
    D. grammar

12. Syntax is: (320)
    A. the analysis of the meaning of individual words.
    B. the study of language.
    C. the study of how words and word groups combine to form phrases, sentences, clauses.
    D. the underlying pattern of words that help convey meaning.

13. A person who is concerned with what the word *love* means in the sentence, "I love roses," is concerned with: (319-320)
    A. grammar.
    B. semantics.
    C. syntax.
    D. phonology.

14. The procedure for solving a problem by implementing a set of rules over and over again until the solution is found is called (304)
    A. logical-reasoning
    B. heuristic
    C. algorithm
    D. problem-solving

15. The problem-solving heuristic that involves breaking a problem down into several smaller steps is called (304)
    A. algorithmic analysis
    B. backward analysis
    C. subgoal analysis
    D. linkage analysis

16. If language is based on biology: (322)
    A. many aspects should be evident early in life.
    B. regardless of culture or language, all children should develop grammar in a similar way.
    C. the role of learning should be permanent.
    D. A and B

17. Mike is planting his garden by looking at a landscaper's drawing of what the finished plants will be like, and buying those plants each year that he can afford and that will get him closest to the drawings. Mike is primarily using which problem-solving heuristic? (304)
    A. functional analysis
    B. hypothetical analysis
    C. subgoal analysis
    D. means-end analysis

18. In problem solving, functional fixedness refers to (304-305)
    A. the ability to fix a problem in your mind and think about it
    B. the failure to realize objects can be used in unusual ways
    C. a tendency to focus on fixing things, even when they work
    D. arranging it so that a solution seems to work, even if it doesn't

19. Lana, the chimpanzee, learned to communicate: (326)
    A. with geometric forms and a computer.
    B. by using sign language.
    C. by humming phonetic sounds.
    D. by arranging symbols on a magnetized board.

20. When do humans begin to develop concepts? (301)
    A. late childhood
    B. infancy
    C. early adolescence
    D. early childhood

21. What is the first stage in problem solving? (303)
    A.  implementing your strategy
    B.  gathering data
    C.  assessing the complexity of the problem
    D.  generating solutions

22. When leaders are accused of lacking creative solutions to problems, they may find it a good idea to try: (307)
    A.  means-end analysis.
    B.  computer simulation.
    C.  brainstorming.
    D.  functional fixedness.

23. Select the major disadvantage of using heuristics to solve problems. (304)
    A.  No solution is guaranteed.
    B.  They are time consuming and inefficient.
    C.  They involve so much effort.
    D.  All of the above

24. A stroke patient knows that an object has a rod and a reel but cannot identify it as a fishing rod.  What key zone does Domasio believe has been corrupted? (313-314)
    A.  divergence
    B.  semantic
    C.  convergence
    D.  parallel

25. In what aspect of language would a psycholinguist most likely be interested? (317)
    A.  phonology
    B.  evolution
    C.  origins
    D.  acquisition

26. What are the basic units of sound that compose the words in a language? (319)
    A.  phonemes
    B.  morphemes
    C.  graphemes
    D.  phones

27. Name the smallest units of speech that contain meaning. (319)
    A.  semantics
    B.  morphemes
    C.  cognates
    D.  phonemes

28. A team of programmers is working to develop a new software system. Which of them is demonstrating mental set? (305)
    A.    one who develops a new technique for graphical displays
    B.    one who figures out a new formula for a certain calculation
    C.    one who uses a program he has used many times before
    D.    one who brings ideas from Eastern philosophy to the project

29. Which of the following cannot be explained by learning theories of language acquisition? (323)
    A.    why children are able to generate sentences they have not heard or used before
    B.    how reinforcement is used to teach language
    C.    why children overgeneralize the concepts expressed in words
    D.    why children imitate adults and other children in their speech

30. Problem-solving processes that focus on finding a single best solution involve_____ thinking; processes that focus on expanding the range of possible solutions involve _____ thinking (307)
    A.    functional; hypothetical
    B.    hypothetical; functional
    C.    divergent; convergent
    D.    convergent; divergent

31. Cognitive psychologists define reasoning as a process by which we (308)
    A.    evaluate situations to reach a conclusion
    B.    decide which member of a category is most "typical"
    C.    express our ideas to other people
    D.    understand how to define a new concept

32. Carlos is going through his college catalogue, trying to select an elective to fulfill his course requirements for next semester. Which cognitive process is Carlos engaged in? (308)
    A.    hypothesis testing
    B.    decision making
    C.    concept formation
    D.    linguistic acquisition

33. Pensacola will probably have a bad hurricane this year because there has not been one since hurricane Erin several years ago. This statement is an example of (309)
    A.    syllogistic thinking
    B.    belief in small numbers
    C.    gambler's fallacy
    D.    critical thinking

34. When people tend to cling to beliefs despite contradictory evidence, psychologists term it (310)
    A.    confirmation bias
    B.    prejudicial bias
    C.    overconfidence
    D.    judgemental

35. The following can be said about the human brain in comparison to the computer: (312)
    A.   the two are not at all compatible
    B.   it has about the same options and ways for processing information
    C.   it has fewer options for information processing
    D.   it has more options and strategies for information processing

36. The view that many different processes are taking place in many different areas of the brain all at the same time is called (314)
    A.   parallel distributed processing
    B.   multiple resource processing
    C.   independent convergent processing
    D.   conditional interlinked processing

37. In psycholinguistics, grammar is a description of (320)
    A.   all the sounds used to speak a language
    B.   how the language functions to generate sentences
    C.   the meanings of all the words in the language
    D.   how children will learn the language in infancy

38. A language acquisition device (LAD) is (323)
    A.   a mechanical device that enhances spoken word for hard of hearing infants
    B.   a procedure that all infants must go through in the acquisition of language
    C.   an innate, unique capacity to acquire and develop language
    D.   a technique used by the Gardners to train Washoe to use sign language

39. Learning theories for the acquisition of language would agree with the importance of which of the following statements (322)
    A.   the language we speak depends on what verbal skills are reinforced
    B.   children must be carefully taught to speak to be healthy
    C.   humans have an inborn ability to learn and use language
    D.   No other animals can use a real language in any way

40. One important difference between the language abilities of chimps and humans is that children will often (326)
    A.   spontaneously point to and name objects
    B.   repeat the same word over and over
    C.   use language to get something that they want
    D.   use words in surprising ways

41. All of the following are true about children's use of language except (327)
    A.   children are born with a predisposition for language
    B.   language acquisition in children is purely biologically-based
    C.   children are reinforced for their language behavior
    D.   language is innate in children

42. The key to understanding language acquisition is to (327)
    A.   consider the structure of language
    B.   analyze the way a child learns language
    C.   study the context in which language is learned and used
    D.   concentrate on the biological basis for language

43. When a part of a neural network is destroyed or removed, the usual result is that the network will  (314-315)
   A.   continue functioning but make some mistakes
   B.   stop functioning but repair itself automatically
   C.   make more and more mistakes until it is useless
   D.   stop functioning completely until it is replaced

44. Computer programs that are able to perform some types of human activities are said to involve (312)
   A.   heuristic algorithms
   B.   linguistic processes
   C.   brain stimulations
   D.   artificial intelligence

45. The tendency to judge the probability of an event by how easy it is to think go examples of it is called (309-310)
   A.   availability heuristic
   B.   overconfidence
   C.   gambler's fallacy
   D.   belief in small numbers

# After You Have Finished

## Essay Questions:

1. Define concept formation and the role of exemplars, fuzzy concepts and prototypes. (301-303)

2. How do neural networks learn and remember? (314-315)

3. Is language innate? Support your answer. (321-323)

4. Describe the 3 qualities of ideas that indicate creativity and how they help with problem solving (306)

5. How do culture and language interact, what research do we have that demonstrates this interaction? (316-317)

# Chapter 10

# Intelligence

## Before you read...

Are you intelligent? Before you can answer that question you must be able to define intelligence. Psychologists have debated for more than 75 years over the definition of intelligence, without agreeing. Various theories have been proposed and probably thousands of intelligence tests have been created. Several people have suggested theories of intelligence, including Spearman, Thurstone, Jensen, Wechsler, and Sternberg. One of the most widely accepted theories is that of David Wechsler. Wechsler's theory defines intelligence as the aggregate or global capacity of an individual to act purposefully, to think rationally, and to deal effectively with the environment. Sternberg's new theory of intelligence challenges the older theories and most intelligence tests. He suggests that a new "practical intelligence" needs to be assessed and tested in our schools. Lefton reports on Goleman's recent publication, Emotional Intelligence, which is said to include self-awareness, impulse control, persistence, self-motivation, ability to recognize emotions in others, and social agility.

Developing a test is a long and complicated process. Proper test development involves standardization and the establishment of test norms. All professional tests must be reliable and valid. Lefton and Brannon examine three important intelligence tests: the Stanford-Binet Intelligence Scale, the Wechsler Scales, and the Kaufman Assessment Battery for Children.

Intelligence testing is not without controversy. Lefton and Brannon introduce the recent book by Hernstein and Murray, *The Bell Curve*. Their book argues that in the United States there exists a cognitive class that is determined by genetic intelligence and is unlikely to change. Critics of intelligence tests have argued for years that the tests are biased and flawed by misinterpretation of the scores. This debate brings back the old nature versus nurture issue and focuses on inherited intelligence. Environmental factors need to be considered as well as cultural differences in the interpretation of intelligence scores. Fortunately, the differences between racial groups are eroding. The chapter concludes with a look at giftedness and mental retardation.

# Chapter Objectives

- Define intelligence and cite the three concepts that are common to most definitions of intelligence.

- Describe the basic features of the major theories of intelligence.

- Examine Goleman's connection between Emotional Intelligence and traditionally defined intelligence.

- Explain how and why psychologists develop standardized tests and describe the types of scores that are obtained from these tests.

- Examine how psychologists ensure that diagnostic tests are reliable and valid and discuss the debate concerning the validity of intelligence testing and the importance of interpretation.

- Characterize the Standford-Binet Intelligence Scale and describe its development.

- Characterize the Wechsler scales of intelligence and compare them with the Stanford-Binet scales.

- Examine the Kaufman Assessment Battery for Children and describe the chief differences between the Kaufman, the Stanford-Binet, and the Wechsler Scales.

- Evaluate the research on test bias to explain why intelligence needs to be considered in a cultural context and how intelligence testing could be changed as a result.

- Discuss ways researchers have investigated the role of the environment and genetics on the development of human traits.

- Summarize the information reported in *The Bell Curve* by Herrnstein and Murray.

- Assess the relative stability of intelligence test scores through the various developmental stages.

- State what researchers have found concerning the differences in test scores between males and females.

- Define giftedness and the 3 factors that should be considered in evaluating giftedness.

- Characterize mental retardation and describe the four levels clinicians use when diagnosing the mentally retarded

# As you read...

## What is Intelligence?

1.    Define Intelligence.

2.    What is Wechler's theory of intelligence?

3.    Describe the two-factor theory of intelligence.

4.    When using statistics to discover mutually independent elements, one is using
_____  _____.

5.    Spearman's basic approach to intelligence is the _____  _____  _____
_____  _____.

6.    What is the factor theory of intelligence?

7.    Define Associate abilities and Cognitive abilities

8.    List Gardner's 8 types of intelligence.

9.    The ability to adapt to, shape and select environments in order to accomplish one's
goals and those of society is referred to as _____ _____.

10.    List and describe Sternberg's 3 dimensions of intelligence.

11. Match the following researchers with the appropriate explanation of their theories of intelligence.

*Wechsler's theory*        **Gardner's view**        *Sternberg's triarchic view*

**Spearman's two-factor theory**        *Jensen's two-level theory*        **Vygotsky's view**

**Thurstone's factor-theory**

A) _____ Claimed that associative and cognitive abilities are inherited.

B) _____ argued that intelligence is not a product rather a process.

C) _____ Believed intelligence consists of general factors (affecting all performance) and specific factors (affecting specific tasks).

D) _____ sees intellectual development in a social context.

E) _____ Has criticized most widely used intelligence tests stating that they are too narrow and don't account for intelligence in the everyday world; believes in multiple types of intelligence.

F) _____ Criticizes IQ tests as being too heavy on linguistic and mathmatical skills.

G) _____ Developed a computational scheme which described seven factors of intelligence such as word fluency, number facility, perceptual speed, reasoning, and spatial visualization.

12.     What are the arguments for a multiple intelligence approach?

13.     What are the arguments for a single intelligence approach?

| 10-2 | **Emotions- A Different Kind of Intelligence?** |
| --- | --- |

14.     What is emotional intelligence?

15.     How does Goleman describe a person with high emotional intelligence?

16.     How does Mayer, Salovey and Caruso's views differ from Goleman's?

# The Process of Test Development

1. Define mental age.

2. Define test.

3. What is the purpose of standardization?

4. What does it mean if something is normally distributed.

5. If your mental age is 14 and your chronological age is 12, what is your IQ?

6. Match the following terms to the appropriate definitions.

   *Standardization*            *normal curve*            *percentile score*
   *Norms*                      *raw score*               *deviation IQ*
   *representative sample*      *standard score*          *intelligence quotient*

   A) _____ A large group of individuals who match the target population (the group for whom the test is being designed) with regard to important variables such as socioeconomic status and age.

   B) _____ Necessary for standardization, these scores and corresponding percentile ranks are obtained by administering the test to the individuals in the representative sample. When the test is released for general use, the scores of those who take the test will be compared to these scores.

   C) _____ The process of developing a uniform procedure for administering and scoring the test. The test is given to a large sample of people who are matched with regard to important variables so that norms can be determined for the basis of comparison. In addition, time limits for testing and specific guidelines for test administration are established.

   D) _____ The number of correct answers an individual receives on the test. To be meaningful this score must be converted, taking into account the individual's age, sex, and grade level.

   E) _____ A bell-shaped curve that provides a graphic illustration of representative test scores. The data are arranged so that those with low scores fall on the left side of the curve; those with middle range scores fall in the middle of the curve (most people achieve scores in the middle ranges); and those with high scores fall on the right side of the curve.

   F) _____ A standard score that indicates what percentage of

185

people in the population under consideration would achieve a lower score.

G) _____ A simple formula to measure intelligence calculated by dividing a person's mental age by the person's chronological age and multiplying the result by 100.

H) _____ A standard score that has the same mean and standard deviation at all ages. Thus, a child of nine and a child of sixteen, each with an IQ of 115, occupy the same position (they have the same percentile score) relative to others who have taken the same IQ test.

I) _____ A score that expresses an individual's position relative to the mean based on the standard deviation. It is often derived by converting a raw score to one that can be interpreted on the basis of a population variable such as age or grade. Two examples of this type of score are a percentile score and a deviation IQ.

## 10-4    Reliability

7.    Define reliability.

8.    Describe the test-retest method.

9.    What are the alternative form and split-half methods?

10.    The number of points a score varies due to imperfect reliability is called _____ _____ _____ _____.

## 10-5    Validity

12.    Define validity.

13.    List and describe the 4 types of validity.

14.    The extent to which a test measures the quality it is supposed to measure is referred to at _____ _____.

15.    What are the 6 criticisms of intelligence test validity?

16.    The _____ _____ is dangerous for teachers because this effect causes one to judge a particular characteristic about a student based on tests of other characteristics.

# Four Important Intelligence Tests

| 10-6    Stanford-Binet Intelligence Scale |
| --- |

1.    Briefly describe the history of the Stanford-Binet Intelligence test.


2.    What are the 4 major subscales of the Stanford-Binet Intelligence test?


3.    Describe the administration of the Stanford-Binet Intelligence test.



| 10-7    Weschler Scales |
| --- |

4.    What are the 3 different Wechsler tests and to whom are they administered?


5.    How are test items grouped in the Weschler scales?


6.    Are scores comparable across ages?



| 10-8    Kaufman Assessment Battery For Children |
| --- |

7.    For what purpose was the K-ABC designed?


8.    List and describe the 4 global scales of the K-ABC.

9. Identify the intelligence test being administered to seven-year-old children in each of the following testing situations.

*Stanford-Binet      WISC-III      K-ABC*

A) _____ By the time the test has been completed, Trystan will have responded to eleven subtests, each of which contains a series of tasks related to a particular content area. One of the subtests, "Comprehension," requires Trystan to verbally answer questions with common sense answers. Another subtest "Picture Completion" requires that he point to the area in a picture that is missing; he does not have to verbally explain what is wrong with the picture. The data gathered from Trystan's responses to the subtests will produce three deviation IQ scores.

B) _____ Sarah is given a variety of tasks that do not call upon her language skills or acquired knowledge, but rather require her to process new information and solve novel problems by organizing, sequencing, and integrating the new stimuli that she is being shown. Toward the end of the test she does have to call upon her verbal ability to answer some questions concerning reading comprehension, word identification, and computation.

C) _____ Aaron is given a variety of tasks that are presented according to his chronological age; the score achieved determines the level at which all other subtests will begin. The content of these subtests varies considerably according to the mental age he is able to achieve. Some of the tasks require verbal responses, others require that he take stimuli presented in the test and call upon his memory, recall, and arranging abilities. When the test is completed, the psychologist will use the data to determine Aaron's mental age.

---

### 10-9    The Woodcock-Johnson

10. What 5 things does the Woodcock-Johnson measure?

11. What are the strengths of the Woodcock-Johnson?

12. Define self-fulfilling prophecy.

13. Describe Rosenthal and Jocobson's research and results.

# Environmental and Biological Factors in Intelligence

## 10-10 Cultural Biases?

14. Define cultural bias.

15. When is a test item or subscale considered to be culturally biased?

16. What evidence is there that intelligences tests are not culturally biased?

## 10-11 Cultural Dimensions of Intelligence

17. What conclusion about culture and intelligence is clear?

18. Why is the typical intelligence test too limited?

19. What are intelligence scores good for?

## 10-12 Environmental and Genetic Impact

20. Define heritability.

21. What does it mean when a trait is 50% heritable.

22. What has research shown about the heritability of intelligence?

23. Describe the evolutionary perspective on intelligence.

## 10-13 The Bell Curve

24. What assertions do the author's of The Bell Curve make about intelligence?

25. What arguments are given against these assertions?

26. What are the weaknesses in Hernstein's and Murray's arguments?

27. Describe the Abecedarian Intervention.

28. What conclusions can be drawn from this research?

## 10-14 Stability of Intelligence Test Scores

29. What is the general pattern of IQ scores throughout the lifespan?

30. What portions of IQ tests show the most change with age?

## 10-15 Are There Gender Differences?

32. What are most gender differences due to?

33. How have these differences been diminished?

34. What differences still exist?

# Exceptionality and Education

## 10-16 Giftedness

1. How does the federal government define gifted and talented?

2. List and describe Renzulli's 3 key factor's for assessing giftedness.

3. What types of programs exist for          gifted students?

4.     Are artistic temperament and bipolar disorder linked?

---

**10-17   Special Education- IDEA**

5.     What is IEP?

6.     What are the basic assumptions of IDEA?

7.     Define mainstreaming.

8.     What is inclusion?

---

**10-18   Mental Retardation**

9.     Define mental retardation.

10.    What 4 things must psychologist who work with the mentally retarded consider?

11.    Match the following types of mental retardation with the appropriate description.

*Mild        Moderate        Severe        Profound*

A) _____ People in this category have the intellectual ability of a ten-year-old. They need some supervision, but can acquire certain academic and occupational skills. The Wechsler IQ range is 55-69 and approximately 90% are classified in this category.

B) _____ People in this category show great motor, speech, and intellectual impairment and are almost totally dependent on others to take care of their basic needs. The retardation is often a result of a birth disorder or traumatic injury to the brain. The Wechsler IQ range is 25-39 and approximately 3% are classified in this category.

C) _____ People in this category are usually institutionalized or dependent on their families. They are somewhat clumsy in motor coordination, posture, and social skills. Their intellectual abilities are comparable to those of a 5 to 6 year-olds. The Wechsler IQ range is 40-54 and approximately 6% are classified in this category.

D) _____ People in this category are institutionalized and need constant supervision. They are unable to master simple skills and have minimal intellectual and motor skills. Frequently they have physical deformities and congenital defects such as blindness, deafness, and seizures. The Wechsler IQ is below 25 and only 1% are classified in this category.

**Term Identification: Make flashcards for each of the following terms.
Hint: Use the definitions in the margins of the chapter**

Intelligence
Factor Analysis
Standardization
Norms
Representative Sample
Normal Curve
Raw Score
Standard Score
Percentile Score

Deviation IQ
Reliability
Validity
Halo Effect
Self-Fulfilling Prophecy
Heritability
Mental Retardation
Mainstreaming

# After you read . . . Self Test

## Chapter 10 Self Test

1. The overall capacity to act purposefully, to think rationally, and to act in the environment is (333)
   A. adapatibility
   B. intelligence
   C. social adaptability
   D. motivation

2. According to a widely accepted definition of intelligence, the most important thing is that it (333)
   A. is inherited genetically from our parents
   B. controls how much information we can retain
   C. determines who will benefit from education
   D. deals with our ability to adapt to our environment

3. A theory of intelligence that emphasizes a person's overall ability to deal successfully with the world was developed by (333)
   A. John Watson
   B. Arthur Jensen
   C. David Wechsler
   D. Robert Sternberg

4. According to Jensen's two-level theory, the intellectual abilities that deal with reasoning and problem solving are called: (334)
   A. associative abilities.
   B. cognitive abilities.
   C. interpersonal abilities.
   D. logical-mathematical abilities.

5. Gardner and Hatch would say that a person who is sensitive to the sounds, rhythms, and meaning of words has a _____ type of intelligence and might choose to be a _____. (335)
   A. musical; composer
   B. spatial; sculptor
   C. interpersonal; therapist
   D. linguistic; poet

6. When Simon and Binet developed their first intelligence test their goal was to: (339)
   A. determine the cause of intelligence.
   B. determine the future of children with high intelligence.
   C. separate children of normal intelligence from those who showed signs of retarded intellectual development.
   D. all of the above

193

7. The first thing a psychologist must decide about a test is: (340)
   A. the mental age of the test subject.
   B. what the test is suppose to measure.
   C. the population for whom a test will be designed.
   D. a uniform procedure for administering and scoring the test.

8. Heather's teacher informed her that 92 percent of her classmates scored lower than she did on an intelligence test. The number 92 represents: (341)
   A. an intelligence quotient.
   B. a standard deviation.
   C. a percentile score.
   D. a raw score.

9. A test intended to measure musical ability should contain items that measure only this ability. In other words, the test should measure what it was intended to measure. This is called: (342)
   A. content validity.
   B. predictive validity.
   C. face validity.
   D. construct validity.

10. Which of the following statements concerning intelligence scales is *false*? (346)
    A. The most recent version of the Stanford-Binet contains items that minimize gender and racial biases.
    B. The WISC-III is administered to adults.
    C. The K-ABC assesses an individual's unique problem solving styles by minimizing the role of language and acquired skills.
    D. Many psychologists consider the K-ABC to be child-oriented and easy to administer.

11. A theory of intelligence that emphasized that a single general factor underlying all intellectual abilities had to be combined with specific factors was developed by (333-334)
    A. Charles Darwin
    B. Louis Thurstone
    C. John Watson
    D. Charles Spearman

12. Vygotsky said that a child's private speech (334)
    A. interfered with the development of logical intellectual abilities
    B. was the basis for understanding the world
    C. must be verbalized before a child can apply it to practical situations
    D. is unrelated to people's ability to use their capabilities in the envornment

13. Which of these intelligence theorists focused not how how much intelligence people have but on how they use it (336)
    A. Louis Thurstone
    B. Charles Spearman
    C. Arthur Jensen
    D. Robert Sternber

14. In Sternberg's triarchic theory of intelligence, the ability to use one's capabilities in a specific situation is_____ intelligence; while the ability to decide what information needs to be processed and how is _____ intelligence.(336-337)
    A. practical; analytic
    B. practical; creative
    C. analytic; creative
    D. creative; analytic

15. According to Goleman, the key to getting ahead in life is (338)
    A. logical and linguistic abilities
    B. intelligence in a cultural context
    C. intellectual skills
    D. emotional intelligence

16. In Binet's original measurement of intelligence, the age level at which a child is functioning intellectually is the child's (339)
    A. chronological age
    B. mental age
    C. intelligence level
    D. general adaptation

17. Intelligence test scores: (354)
    A. begin to gradually decrease beginning around age 40.
    B. generally reach their peak when a child learns to talk.
    C. tend to increase with age and level off in adulthood.
    D. of 10 year-old chimpanzees correlate well to those of average 3 year-old humans.

18. A group of people taken from a larger population who match the population on all important variables is said to be a (340)
    A. social norm
    B. representative sample
    C. control group
    D. correlation coefficient

19. When measurements of a variable come out with most of the scores in the middle, and fewer as you go higher and lower, we ay that the scores are (340)
    A. normally distributed
    B. analytically arranged
    C. statistically reliable
    D. computationally independant

20. A diagnosis of mental retardation requires: (359)
    A. an IQ score below a 70.
    B. difficulty adapting to the environment.
    C. symptoms of hyperactivity.
    D. both A and B are correct.

21. A test score that expresses how an individual scored relative to other similar people is the (340)
    A. cumulative score
    B. collective score
    C. standard score
    D. raw score

22. When a child is placed in a mainstreaming educational system the child typically: (358)
    A. stays in a regular classroom setting for at least half of the school day.
    B. is placed in school with other children who are mentally retarded.
    C. is labeled according to his or her mental age level and level of retardation.
    D. has only one teacher and learns on a one-to-one basis.

23. Sandy is 10 years old. A standardized IQ test measured Sandy's mental age as 11. This means that Sandy's IQ score would be (341)
    A. 110
    B. 95
    C. 11
    D. 80$^{th}$ percentile

24. To control the amount of variability in IQ scores for children of different ages, tests today use a kind of score called a (341)
    A. raw score
    B. mental age
    C. deviation IQ
    D. variability score

25. What is standardization used to determine? (340)
    A. achievement
    B. test norms
    C. reliability
    D. validity

26. What will the standard error of measurement be on a highly reliable standardized test? (342)
    A. significant
    B. variable
    C. valid
    D. small

27. When one particular or outstanding characteristic about an individual is allowed to influence evaluations, this is called a: (343)
    A. singular advantage.
    B. blooming effect.
    C. corona significance.
    D. halo effect.

28. Giving someone two different versions of the same test on two different occasions and comparing the scores is a _____ measure of reliability (342)
    A. content
    B. alternate-form
    C. split-half
    D. test-retest

29. The SAT is a standardized test of knowledge, skills, and reasoning ability for college applicants. If students who score well on this test are in fact more successful at college than those with low scores, then this test has high (342)
    A. predictive validity
    B. retest reliability
    C. normal distributions
    D. cultural fairness

30. Critics claim that IQ tests cannot really measure intelligence, because psychologists have not even decided on a definition of what intelligence is. Defender of IQ tests point out that these tests have high (342-343)
    A. face validity
    B. test-retest validity
    C. cultural fairness
    D. predictive ability

31. The current version of the Stanford-Binet Intelligence Scale has_____ subscales and _____ possible subtests. (345)
    A. 3; 30
    B. 2; 30
    C. 4; 15
    D. 3; 7

32. What happens to IQ scores during adulthood? (354)
    A. steadily decrease
    B. usually show significant increases
    C. remain relatively stable
    D. change more than during childhood

33. Which view of intelligence uses correlations between items to uncover common underlying abilities? (333-334)
    A. Jensen's two-level theory
    B. Gardener's multiple intelligences
    C. Factor theories
    D. Wechsler's theory

34. According to Sternberg's triarchic theory of intelligence, someone who has common sense is high in which kind of intelligence? (336)
    A. Analytic
    B. Practical
    C. Creative
    D. Successful

35. Todd wants to know what proportion of the people who took the SAT scored better than he did. Which type of score should he look at? (341)
    A. percentile score
    B. raw score
    C. standard score
    D. deviation score

36. Which term describes an intelligence test that consistently produces the same score on different occasions? (341)
    A. Norms
    B. Reliability
    C. Validity
    D. Standardization

37. According to the Stanford-Binet Intelligence Scale, IQ is based on a child's: (344-345)
    A. mental age
    B. chronological age
    C. both a and b
    D. neither

38. Who was responsible for an intelligence test designed to test adults? (345-346)
    A. Binet
    B. Stanford
    C. Kaufman
    D. Wechsler

39. Which set of percentages most accurately describes the relationship between heredity and environment in determining intelligence? (351)
    A. 10% heredity: 90% environment
    B. 50% heredity: 50% environment
    C. 75% heredity: 25% environment
    D. 90% heredity: 10% environment

40. The Kaufman Assessment Battery for Children was designed specifically to (346)
    A. give children scores that are comparable to adults
    B. provide a well-standardized, stable intelligence score
    C. measure verbal, mathematical, and logical reasoning
    D. apply equally well to people of many different cultures

41. The majority of all retarded persons are classified in the ___ level of retardation. (359)
    A. profound
    B. moderate
    C. mild
    D. severe

42. The passage of Public Law 94-142 states that all school-age children be provided with appropriate and free public education. For those with mental retardation, this means: (358)
    A. special schools must be created for mentally retarded children
    B. mainstreaming must occur when possible
    C. mentally retarded children must be included in the social aspect of schooling
    D. they must not be tested any more than normal children

43. Research on the issue of cultural and racial bias in intelligence tests supports the viewpoint that (349)
    A. they are systematically biased against African Americans
    B. they are systematically biased against women
    C. they are systematically biased against low-income people
    D. there are no systematic biases in the tests themselves

44. Based on research on IQ tests in many different cultures, the author strongly concludes that (350)
    A. there is a genetic component to our intelligence levels
    B. all current IQ tests exhibit systematic ethnic and cultural bias
    C. IQ tests measure a person's adaptability to his or her culture
    D. a person's intelligence is fixed at birth and can't be changed

45. The genetically determined proportion of a trait's variation among individuals in a population is (350)
    A. genotype
    B. heritability
    C. phenotype
    D. asymmetry

# After You Have Finished

## Essay Questions:

1. Define reliability and validity and why they are important. (341-343)

2. Describe the Weschler Scales and their advantage over the Stanford-Binet. (345-346)

3. Describe factors that may lead to mental retardation. (359)

4. How do cognitive abilities and emotional intelligence interact? (338)

5. Describe the criticisms of motivation to succeed and stereotype threat to IQ tests and how defenders of IQ tests respond to these criticisms (343)

# Chapter 11

# Motivation and Emotion

# Before you read...

Psychologists and people in general are always asking the question: Why? To answer the question we must try to understand the interacting forces behind specific behaviors and accept that no one theory or explanation will fit all situations. Motivation is an internal condition that exhibits itself as goal-directed behavior. Several theories exist to explain people's motivation. Drive theory assumes that an organism is motivated by some internal need to survive. Arousal theory assumes that we have a need to maintain an optimal level of central nervous system arousal. Expectancy theory states that we are driven by our thoughts and expectations for success. Cognitive theory also endorses the contribution of thoughts, but adds that people are actively involved in determining their goals and means to achieve them. This approach focuses on the decision making process and begins to move away from the mechanistic theories of physiological needs toward an understanding of intrinsic and extrinsic motivations. Humanistic theory focuses on human dignity, individual choice, and self-worth. Humanists are looking at the big picture, stating that people strive toward a lifelong goal of self-actualization.

Hunger is certainly a true physiological need. Or is it? We all know the feeling of being hungry you may get stomach pangs, begin to feel weak, or even become lightheaded. Your body is sending signals that it is time to eat. The glucostatic approach to explaining hunger argues that food deprivation leads to low blood sugar and results in a chemical imbalance that is cured by eating. The goal of eating is to maintain a balance. The problem with the balance approach is it does not fully explain problem eating, obesity, or eating disorders such as anorexia nervosa and bulimia nervosa. Lefton and Brannon describe the relationship between hunger and obesity by first looking at the genetic contribution and then examining the findings of Schacter's research on the role of external cues in overeating.

Sexual behavior in animals is relatively straightforward. Animals' sexual behavior is driven by their hormones. However, it is not so simple in humans. Many factors contribute to sexual behavior in humans; sights, sounds, smells, thoughts, feelings, and even fantasy have the potential to initiate or satisfy sexual motivation. Lefton and Brannon look at classic research on human sexual behavior starting with the Kinsey studies in the 40s and 50s, and continuing to the more contemporary works of Hunt, Masters and Johnson, and Laumann. These studies surveyed a variety of sexual behaviors including sexual orientation. Lefton and Brannon also examine the need for achievement (social need) and how these achievement motives are measured.

Emotions by definition are subjective responses accompanied by a physiological change. Many psychologists claim that emotions consist of three basic elements: feelings, physiological responses, and behaviors. Others describe emotions in terms of types, levels or additional elements. Few take all of these elements into account in their research, so we must examine emotions by their components. The *limbic system* is thought to contribute to emotions by integrating information at the neuronal level resulting in an emotional response. The two physiological theories of emotion, James-Lange and Cannon-Bard, describe this process in terms of the physiological and emotional response. They differ as to which comes first. Physiological expression of emotion can be monitored by use of a polygraph, which is based on the premise that autonomic nervous system responses are involuntary.

Cognitive theories of emotion focus on the interpretation as well as the physiological response. For example, the Schachter-Singer approach looked at incorporating both the James-Lange and Canon-Bard theories, stating that the context of the situation must be considered. Other researchers, such as Valins, Reisenzein, Shaver, and Ekman, express their points of view on this complex topic. In closing, Lefton and Brannon look at the universality of behavioral expressions and whether we have the ability to control our emotions.

# Chapter Objectives

- Describe the basic components of motivation.

- Outline drive theories and discuss how animals and human beings strive to maintain homeostasis.

- Specify how arousal and sensory stimulation needs differ from other biological needs and describe how various levels of arousal and anxiety affect performance.

- Discuss expectancy theories and compare them with drive and arousal theories.

- Describe the cognitive theory of motivation and examine the degree of voluntary control people have over their emotions.

- Outline Abraham Maslow's theory of motivation, describe self-actualization, and discuss how humanistic theory deals with cultural differences.

- Discuss the physiological determinants of hunger, focusing on the role of the hypothalamus.

- Compare the genetic and physiological explanations of obesity and overeating.

- Be able to discuss how hormones, sights, sounds, smells, and fantasies may initiate sex drive in humans.

- Briefly describe the human sexual response cycle.

- Compare and contrast the findings of the Kinsey studies and the Lauman studies as they relate to human sexual behavior and discuss the nature-versus-nurture debate in relation to sexual orientation in humans.

- Define what is meant by need for achievement and why it is important; describe how tests are used to describe people with high or low needs for achievement and how need for achievement is related to the amount of risk people are willing to take.

- Describe emotion from a psychological perspective; also list and describe the elements of emotion often studied by psychologists.

- Distinguish between James-Lange and Cannon-Bard physiological theories of emotion.

- Describe the Schachter-Singer, Valins, Shaver, and Frijda cognitive explanations of emotion.

# As you read...

## Theories of Motivation

1. Define motivation.


2. List and describe the 4 basic parts of motivation.


---

**11-1     Evolutionary Theories**

3. Define instinct.


4. What is the evolutionary view of motivation and emotion?


---

**11-2     Drive Theories**

5. Define drive.


6. What is a need?


7. _____ _____ explains behavior that an organism is motivated to act because of a need to maintain the organism or the species.


8. Define homeostasis.


9. The goal that satisfies a need is often referred to as _____.


10. Define conflict.


11. Describe the 3 types of conflict.


12. What 3 principles does Miller give for predicting behavior in conflict situation?

13.     Define arousal.

14.     Why was arousal theory formed?

15.     Describe the Yerkes-Dodson law.

16.     How does Hebb view arousal?

17.     Define cognitive theories.

18.     What are expectancy theories?

19.     Define motive.

20.     What is a social need?

21.     Describe intrinsic and extrinsic motivation.

22.     Motivation due to the presence of rewards is called _____ _____.

23.     Describe the overjustification effect.

24.     Define humanistic theory.

25.     Describe self-actualization.

26.     Describe Maslow's hierarchy.


27.     Complete the following table.

| Theory | Theorist | Explains | Key Idea | View of Behavior |
|---|---|---|---|---|
| | Cosmides & Tooby | | Instincts apply even more to humans than other animals | |
| Drive | Hull | | | Largely Mechanistic |
| | Miller | Conflict among motivations | | |
| | Hebb | | Performance depends on the level of arousal | |
| Cognitive | | Achievement motivation | Humans learn the need to achieve | |
| | Deci | Intrinsic motivation | | |
| Humanistic | | | Self-Actualization | |

# Hunger: A Physiological Need

## 11-6    Physiological Determinants of Hunger

1.     What is a set point?


2.     What are the 2 necessary components for homeostatic weight control?


3.     List and describe the 2 hormones important to maintaining weight balance.


4.     Eating begins _____ the body's energy levels become low.

1.      Why do we feel hungry?


5.      What influences food preferences?


6.      _____ is another factor in eating even when one is not hungry.

7.      What is the rate of clinical obesity in America?


8.      Describe the evolutionary perspective on obesity.


9.      List and describe 2 inherited traits that can lead to obesity.


10.     Give the 4 key factors to overeating.


# Sexual Behavior

11.     What are androgens and estrogens, where are they produced, and what is their purpose?


12.     Define pheromones.


13      How are sights sounds and fantasy involved in sex drive?

14.     Define the sexual response cycle.

15.     Identify the phase involving the sexual response cycle.

        *Excitement    Plateau    Orgasm    Resolution.*

A) _____ The stage of the sexual response cycle in which both men and women are preparing for orgasm.

B) _____ The stage of the sexual response cycle in which the body naturally returns to its resting or normal state.

C) _____ The stage of the sexual response cycle in which there are initial increases in heart rate, blood pressure, and respiration.

D) _____ The stage of the sexual response cycle in which the autonomic nervous system activity reaches its peak, and muscle contractions occur throughout the body in spasms.

16.     What is the refractory period?

---

**11-11   Human Sexual Behavior**

17.     Define survey?

18.     What is a representative sample?

19.     Describe Laumann's research and conclusions.

20.     How have sexual behavior differences between men and woman decreased?

21.     Describe the picture of sexuality in the United States.

22.     Define sexual dysfunction.

23.     Describe the 3 types of sexual orientation.

24.     What evidence does research provide for biological determinates of sexual orientation?

25.     What evidence does research provide for environmental determinates of sexual orientation?

# Achievement: A Social Need

1.      cribe the need for achievement.


2.      How is achievement motivation different in Asian and Western cultures?


3.      Describe the TAT.


4.      What is the OSCI?


5.      High _____ _____, the belief that one can successfully engage in and execute a specific behavior is common in people with high need for achievement.

# Emotion

| 11-12  What is Emotion? |
|---|

6.      Define emotion.


7.      What are the 3 components of emotion?


| 11-13  Physiological Theories of Emotion |
|---|

8.      Describe the limbic system.


9.      Define sham rage


10.      Describe the James-Lange Theory of emotions.


11.      What is the facial feedback hypothesis.


12.      Describe the Cannon-Bard Theory of emotions.

13.     Describe the two routes Ledoux gives for emotional experiences.


14.     What is the importance of the amygdala?


15.     What is the evolutionary view of emotion?


16.     How does the evolutionary view about positive emotions?


## 11-14   Cognitive Theories of Emotion


17.     Describe the Schachter-Singer Approach.


18.     Describe Schachter and Singer's 1962 experiments.


19.     Identify the theory that most adequately explains why the particular emotion in the following situations is experienced.

| | |
|---|---|
| *LeDoux's emotional brain* | *Cannon-Bard* |
| *James-Lange* | *Schachter-Singer* |

A)  _____ Barry lacks his usual energy level, does not have any appetite though he has not eaten for some time, and has trouble concentrating and going to sleep.  Based on this feedback from his body, Barry is aware that he is *depressed*.

B)  _____ While discussing a pay raise with her boss, Tanya feels an awkward and odd feeling inside but is not certain what she is feeling or why.  When she recounts the conversation, she realizes that her boss had subtly accused her of being lazy on the job.  Based on this information she told herself she is feeling *embarrassed*.

C)  _____.While walking to class Samantha hears what appears to be either firecrackers or maybe gunshots coming from the next hallway.  She begins to feel herself sweat and she is confused.  She decides to stay where she is and hope the incident will not involve her.

D)  _____ Olga sits in her hot tub and as her muscles begin to relax, she begins to feel *peacefully content*.

20.     Describe the Lazaruz Approach.

21.    Define appraisal.

22.    List Izard's 10 basic emotions.

23.    What are display rules?

24.    What cultural differences were seen in the Sherer survey?

25.    Define individualistic and collectivist cultures.

26.    How are emotions viewed differently in individualist and collectivist cultures?

27.    Describe the gender stereotypes about emotion.

28.    Why are these stereotypes inaccurate?

29.    What is a polygraph device?

30.    Describe how the polygraph works.

31.    Can people beat the polygraph?

32.    What is the easiest component of emotion to control?

33.    Describe Tice's research on impulse control.

**Term Identification: Make flashcards for each of the following terms. Hint: Use the definitions in the margins of the chapter**

Motivation

Drive Theory

Drive

Need

Homeostasis

Conflict

Approach-Approach Conflict

Avoidance-Avoidance Conflict

Approach-Avoidance Conflict

Arousal

Cognitive Theories

Expectancy Theories

Motive

Social Need

Extrinsic Motivation

Intrinsic Motivation

Overjustification Effect

Humanistic Theory

Self-Actualization

Excitement Phase

Vasocongestion

Plateau Phase

Orgasm Phase

Resolution Phase

Survey

Representative Sample

Need For Achievement

Self-Efficacy

Emotion

Appraisal

# After you read . . . Self Test

## Chapter 11 Self Test

1. Which of the following is not one of the four basic parts of motivation? (366)
    A. observed by inference
    B. goal directed behavior
    C. external condition
    D. initiation, activation, or maintenance

2. That organisms are motivated by needs is a statement of: (367)
    A. drive theory.
    B. mechanistic theory.
    C. a drive.
    D. drive state.

3. A state of psychological imbalance is called a(n) (367)
    A. drive
    B. need
    C. impulse
    D. trigger

4. When Meghan's parents caught her aggravating her sister, she was given the option of two consequences, loss of a privilege or quiet time in her room. Meghan was faced with a (369)
    A. Approach-Avoidance conflict
    B. Approach-Approach conflict
    C. Avoidance-Approach conflict
    D. Avoidance-Avoidance conflict.

5. The state that results when people have to make a difficult choice is called (368)
    A. frustration
    B. conflict
    C. arousal
    D. anxiety

6. Maggie is considering leaving her abusive husband. Leaving would bring her physical security, but she has no job skills to support herself. Maggie is faced with a(n) _____ conflict (369)
    A. approach-approach
    B. avoidance-avoidance
    C. approach-avoidance
    D. double approach-avoidance

7. A state that involve activation of the central nervous system, the autonomic nervous system and the muscles and glands is called (369)
   A. motivation
   B. expectancy
   C. arousal
   D. homestasis

8. If a behavior that is intrinsically rewarding is first rewarded and then those rewards are stopped, its occurrence is decreased. That is called the (372-373)
   A. overt cost of rewards
   B. covert cost of rewards
   C. overregularization effect
   D. overjustification effect

9. Researchers who explain motivation in terms of an optimal level of arousal assume that individuals seek an optimal level of arousal; thus, people who show a _____ anxiety level and arousal tend to produce the most and do best. (370)
   A. high
   B. moderate
   C. low
   D. A and C

10. Hebb's idea focused on _____ in determining behavior. (371)
    A. people's response
    B. stimuli
    C. drives
    D. needs

11. Human males sex hormones are _____ while female sex hormones are _____ (381)
    A. androgens; estrogens
    B. estrogens; androgens
    C. pheromones; cholesterones
    D. cholesterones; pheromones

12. A social need is an aroused condition involving all but feelings about: (371)
    A. relationships.
    B. goals.
    C. self.
    D. others.

13. At the age of 40, Dmitri suffered an injury that resulted in the complete removal of both of his testes. The most likely result of this removal on Dmitri's sexual activity is that (381)
    A. he will no longer become sexually aroused
    B. he will no longer be able to perform the sex act
    C. he will no longer feel pleasure with this orgasm
    D. there will be no major change in his sexual activity

14. Compares with the sexual behavior of lower organisms, the sexual behavior of humans is (381)
    A.   much more violent and uncontrolled
    B.   more controlled by biology
    C.   more affected by hormone levels
    D.   less affected by hormone levels

15. Vasocongestion, or engorgement of blood vessels in the genital area, is usually a sign of (382)
    A.   the beginnings of a person's orgasm
    B.   an abnormally high level of hormones
    C.   the beginnings of sexual arousal
    D.   a problem that interferes with sexual activity

16. Cognitive theory focuses on _____ as initiators and determiners of behavior. (371)
    A.   sensory stimulation
    B.   external cues
    C.   thoughts
    D.   arousal

17. Creating objects in your spare time because it gives you a sense of pleasure and accomplishment is probably motivated by: (372)
    A.   extrinsic reward.
    B.   intrinsic reward.
    C.   a need for achievement.
    D    a Type B personality.

18. According to Maslow's pyramid of needs, the very first needs that must be met are _____ needs. (374)
    A.   love and recognition
    B.   recognition and approval
    C.   physiological and safety
    D.   cognitive and aesthetic

19. Maslow's humanistic theory of motivation: (374-375)
    A.   rejects drive theories.
    B.   is an expectancy theory.
    C.   is a unique theory that has nothing in common with the other theories discussed in the chapter.
    D.   incorporates the best elements of drive, expectancy, and cognitive theories.

20. Which of the following is *not* included in the definition of emotion?  Emotions: (388)
    A.   have motivating properties that impel and direct behavior.
    B.   have a private, personal, unique, and subjective component.
    C.   are the result of irrational thoughts.
    D.   are generally accompanied by physiological changes.

21. The period of time after an orgasm during which a man is unable to achieve another erection is called the (382)
    A.    refractory period
    B.    exhaustion stage
    C.    plateau phase
    D.    down time

22. Whose theory states that people do not experience emotion until after their bodies become aroused? (390)
    A.    Cannon's
    B.    James-Lange
    C.    Schachter-Singer
    D.    Shaver's

23. Neither the James-Lange nor the Cannon-Bard approach considered the idea that a person's _____ might alter their reaction/response to a situation. (390)
    A.    motivation
    B.    arousal
    C.    emotional state
    D.    thoughts

24. Laumann's study of sexual practices found that _____ of men had had extramarital affairs (383)
    A.    75%
    B.    90%
    C.    25%
    D.    10%

25. One general finding of most scientific research on American sexual attitudes and behaviors is that (383)
    A.    people have more sexual activities when they are younger
    B.    very few women engage in premarital sexual activity
    C.    most people are unsatisfied with the quality of their sex lives
    D.    there are more male homosexuals than people realize

26. A social need that directs people to work for excellence and success is called (386)
    A.    inspiration
    B.    a need for achievement
    C.    the apperception motive
    D.    self-actualization

27. For adults who show a high need for achievement, a typical pattern of their childhood experiences is that (386)
    A.    a need for achievement developed in high school
    B.    they got lower than average grades in elementary school
    C.    their parents praised them for their achievements
    D.    they were the same as people with low achievement needs

28. One way to measure the need for achievement is through the Thematic Apperception Test (TAT), which involves asking people to (387)
    A.   tell about their childhood experiences
    B.   describe their own attitudes and opinions
    C.   select the alternatives that are more true for them
    D.   answer questions about vague, ambiguous pictures

29. Lie detectors record: (398)
    A.   voluntary physiological changes.
    B.   emotional states.
    C.   autonomic nervous system activity.
    D.   involuntary physiological changes.

30. What do the four aspects of the definition of motivation include? (366)
    A.   biologically significant
    B.   response to an incentive
    C.   an internal condition
    D.   all of the above

31. What part of the brain regulates eating behavior? (376)
    A.   hypothalamus
    B.   amygdala
    C.   superior colliculus
    D.   reticular formation

32. Name the stage of the sexual response cycle in which the body returns to its normal state. (382)
    A.   post-orgasmic
    B.   refractory
    C.   recovery
    D.   resolution

33. Which of the following is a key element in expectancy theory? (371)
    A.   Thoughts guide behavior.
    B.   Physiological drives are of little importance in human behavior.
    C.   Emotions can be motives.
    D.   Motives can be reinforced.

34. Which term refers to behavior that people engage in for no reward other than the pleasure of the activity itself? (372)
    A.   achievement motivated
    B.   power motivated
    C.   extrinsically motivated
    D.   intrinsically motivated

35. How would early motivation theorists have described the needs at the base of Maslow's pyramid? (373-374)
    A. social motives
    B. drives
    C. expectations
    D. incentives

36. What theory of emotion suggests that smiling can make people happy? (390)
    A. Cannon-Bard
    B. Shoaf-Strouss
    C. James-Lange
    D. Schacter-Singer

37. What do polygraphs measure? (398)
    A. arousal
    B. honesty
    C. lies
    D. all of the above

38. Motivation is considered an internal condition that initiates behavior and we infer the link to external behaviors. The fourth criteria for motivation is that behavior is (366)
    A. abstract
    B. concrete
    C. goal directed
    D. arousal based

39. Which theory of motivation assumes a need for balance or homeostasis? (367)
    A. drive theory
    B. cognitive theory
    C. arousal theory
    D. humanistic theory

40. _____ theory of motivation assumes that people take an active role in determining their goals and the means to achieve them. (371)
    A. expectancy theory
    B. cognitive theory
    C. social theory
    D. drive theory

41. When you engage in behavior for some external gain, the behavior is said to be _____ _____. When you engage in behavior for the internal pleasure, the behavior is said to be _____ _____. (372)
    A. social need; motive driven
    B. extrinsically motivated; intrinsically motivated
    C. goal directed; pleasure directed
    D. self actualization; overjustification effect

42. Sexual behavior in humans can be initiated by (380)
    A. fantasy, thoughts, emotions
    B. hormones, smells, need
    C. excitement, hormones, desire
    D. pheromones, desire, excitement

43. The largest difference in the results of the Kinsey report (1950) and the Laumann report (1998) was the later report suggests (384)
    A. more female homosexuals
    B. more male homosexuals
    C. more bisexual behavior
    D. less male homosexuality

44. Most psychologist now agree that emotions consist of three basic elements. They include (388)
    A. subjective response; physical behavior; cognition
    B. feelings; physiological response; behavior
    C. love; fear; anger
    D. fear; anger; sadness

45. The following theory of emotion contends that emotions are cognitive based and thought alone can elicit an emotion (393-394)
    A. Canon-Bard
    B. Schacter-Singer
    C. Valins-Reisenzein
    D. James-Lange

# When You Have Finished

## Essay Questions:

1.    What is Hebb's view on motivation?(371)

2.    How does Maslow view motivation? (373-374)

3.    Are emotional facial expressions universal? Support your answer. (392-393)

4.    What are the two hormones important in weight maintenance and where are they produced? (376)

5.    Describe Tice's research and findings with breakdowns of impulse control. (399)

# Chapter 12

# Personality and Its Assessment

## Before you read...

What do you think of when you hear your friends describing someone you've never met? Personality is a set of relatively enduring behavioral characteristics and internal predispositions that describe how a person reacts to the environment. Theories of personality and personality development abound. Theories attempt to explain the role of nature and nurture, the presence of unconscious processes, and the stability and consistencies of these behaviors.

Sigmund Freud's psychoanalytic theory offers a perspective on how the unconscious is involved in our behavior; his ideas continue to influence modern theories. There are three levels of consciousness described as the conscious, the preconscious, and the unconscious. Freud also believed that the *id*, *ego*, and *superego* are the structures of the personality and that conflict arises among these components. Freud claims that personality develops through a series of five stages: oral, anal, phallic, latency, and genital. Unresolved conflicts that occur during these stages may develop into fixations if the individual inappropriately uses defense mechanisms to attempt to resolve the conflict. Freud's theory must be considered in the context from which it came. The original theory influenced many later theorists, one group of whom is called the neo-Freudians. Carl Jung proposed that we all have a collective unconscious that is a shared storehouse of inherited images and ideas. Adler suggested that we all strive to overcome inferiority in order to fulfill ourselves; the social nature of individuals was more important to Adler than Freud proposed.

Behavioral approaches to personality are based on learning, and on the idea that our personality is a result of learning from our environment. They focus on overt behaviors rather than covert mechanisms. The approach relies heavily on precise definitions of behaviors and practical approaches to changing or relearning different responses. Classical conditioning, operant conditioning, and observational learning are obvious contributors to the behavioral approach to personality.

Lefton an Brannon examine the trait and type theories of Allport, Cattell, and Eysenck. Allport decided that traits could be divided into three categories: the *cardinal* traits, those that determine one's direction in life; the *central* traits, the basic units of one's personality; and, the *secondary* traits, those which are situation specific. Cattell used factor analysis to cluster traits into what he termed *surface* traits and *source* traits. Eysenck focused at a higher level. He determined that traits were organize into types and that there were three basic dimensions of this organization, emotional stability, introversion-extroversion, and psychoticism. Finally, the "*Big Five*" theory attempts to blend the trait and type theories into five supertraits. This theory proposes that personality can be described by looking at five broad categories: extroversion-introversion, agreeableness-antagonism, conscientiousness-undirectedness, neuroticism-stability, and openness to experience.

Humanistic theories were developed in response to Freud's theory. Humanists like Maslow and Rogers emphasize the importance of people's interpretation of the world. Maslow's theory of self-actualization focuses on what one might achieve. Rogers' key concepts center around the ideal self and the real self. He stressed the importance of agreement between one's view of the ideal and real self. Appropriate self-concept is a result of this agreement.

The cognitive approach accepts the behavioral premise and adds a new dimension. Cognitive psychologists emphasize the interactive role of thought process and behavior. One of the conceptual frameworks used to describe the cognitive approach is that of *self-schemata* or global themes that we use to describe ourselves. Rotter's *locus of control* is another view of how individuals with an internal locus of control differ from those with an external locus-of-control in personality. Bandura submits that a person's belief or expectancy for success determines the types of behavior undertaken. Mischel also believed thought was important, but added that through a process called *self-regulation* people learned to interact with their environment in flexible ways. This chapter also considers the stability of shyness and the changes in women's personality through the lifespan.

The last section in this chapter looks at personality assessment. Psychologists may use objective instruments such as the popular MMPI/MMPI-2, which are self report types of tests, or they may use projective tests like the Rorschach inkblots which attempt to reveal unconscious motives, or they may use the behavioral assessment method of recording overt behaviors. Most psychologists will use some combination of these techniques to assess individual personalities and determine treatment plans.

# Chapter Objectives

- Define the term *personality,* and cite the five key questions that personality theorists ask in describing personality.

- Describe Freud's three levels of consciousness and the mental forces he said explained causes of behavior. Describe Freud's psychosexual stage theory of personality development.

- Identify the major defense mechanisms and explain how people use these to reduce anxiety. Explain how Freud's theory has been a major influence on psychology and Western culture.

- Examine the basic assumptions of Adler's personality theory and explain how his fulfillment approach and the social nature of human beings contribute to this theory.

- Describe the issues on which Jung differs from Freud and summarize the concepts for which Jung's theory is most noted.

- Describe the behavioral approach to personality development and state how it differs from other personality theories.

- Compare and contrast Allport's and Cattell's trait theories.

- List the three basic dimensions of Eysenck's type theory

- List and differentiate the "supertraits" known as the Big Five.

- Explain Maslow's pyramidal hierarchy in terms of how self-actualization is involved in the development of personality.

- Identify Rogers' basic assumptions about personality and its development and state his definition of the relationship between personality and the self.

- Characterize some of the assumptions made by cognitive personality theorists and explain how this theory differs from the traditional behavioral model.

- Explain the importance of having a strong sense of self-efficacy; how this aspect of personality develops, according to Bandura; and how gender norms can influence it.

- Discuss how Mischel's self-regulatory process allows people to respond flexibly to various situations.

- Define what is meant by a personality inventory and identify some of the most popular instruments used in personality assessment. Outline the major differences between objective and projective personality tests.

# As you read...

## What Is Personality?

1.   Define personality.


2.   List 5 questions personality research and theory should be able to answer.


## Psychodynamic Theories

| 12-1   The Psychoanalytic Theory of Sigmund Freud |

1.   Define Oedipus Complex.


2.   What is psychoanalysis.


3.   Describe and the 5 assumptions of psychoanalysis.


4.   Match the following levels of consciousness with the appropriate definition.
       *Preconscious    Unconscious   Conscious*
   A) _____ The thoughts, feelings, and actions a person is *aware* of. This is the first level of consciousness and is very easy to study and understand.
   B) _____ Mental activity (thoughts and feelings) that a person can become aware of if they closely pay attention to them. This is the second level of consciousness; it takes a little time and effort to study and understand it.
   C) _____ Thoughts and feelings beyond normal awareness. This is the third level of consciousness; so deeply repressed, it can be studied and understood only by spending a lot of time and effort using a technique like psychoanalysis, according to Freud.

5.   List and describe the 3 basic structures of the mind?


6.   Define the pleasure principle

7.     The _____ works by the _____ _____ and attempts to check the power of the id.

8.     Describe ego ideal and conscience.

9.     List and describe Freud's 5 stages of personality development.

11.    The _____ stage focuses on children's ability to have control of their bodily functions, thereby learning control and orderliness as adults.

12.    The _____ _____ deals with feelings of rivalry between the same sex parent.

13.    Describe how the Oedipus complex is resolved?

14.    During the _____ _____, the feelings of sexuality, fear, and repressed feelings of earlier stages come out.

15.    What are Freud's 2 great drives?

16.    Define libido.

17.    What is a defense mechanism?

18.    List and describe the 8 types of defense mechanisms.

19.    Match the following defense mechanisms to the appropriate definition.
       *repression    projection    denial    reaction formation*
       *rationalization    sublimation*
       A) _____ Making unreasonable feelings and behaviors seem reasonable by reinterpreting them.
       B) _____ Refusing to accept reality and the true source of anxiety.
       C) _____ Attributing one's own undesirable traits to others.
       D) _____ Behaving in a manner that is opposite to one's true, but anxiety-producing, feelings.

E) _____ Anxiety-producing feelings are blocked from conscious awareness and pushed into the unconscious. For Freud this defense mechanism was the most important to understand.

F) _____ Energy from an impulse that might be considered taboo is channeled or redirected into a socially acceptable form.

20.    How does Westin defend Freud's theory?


| 12-2 | **Adler and Individual Psychology** |

21.    Define individual psychology.

22.    List and describe the 6 concepts of Adler's theory.

23.    Describe Adler's style of life.

24.    Adler terms the feeling of oneness with all of humanity _____ _____.

25.    What is the role of early recollections in Adler's therapy?


| 12-3 | **Jung and Analytical Psychology** |

26.    Compare and contrast Jung's theory with Freud's theory.

27.    Define collective unconscious.

28.    What are archetypes?

29.    List and describe the 4 important archetypes.

30._____ _____is the archetype of nourishment and destruction.

31. What is a mandala?

# Skinner and Behavioral Analysis

| 12-4 | The Power of Learning |
|---|---|

1. How do behaviorists look at personality?

2. Define operant conditioning?

3. What are positive and negative reinforcers?

4. List the two types of punishment.

| 12-5 | Acquiring a Personality |
|---|---|

5. How do learning theorists think personality is acquired?

6. How is survival important in this process?

7. How is culture involved in this process?

# Trait and Type Theories: Stable Behavioral Dispositions

1. What is a trait?

2. Define a longitudinal study?

3. Describe the research of Charles and her conclusions.

4. What are types?

## 12-6 Allport's Personal Disposition Theory

1. Define personal dispositions.

2. Describe the 3 categories of traits given by Allport.

3. Describe Allport's cardinal, central, and secondary *traits* and give an example of each.

    A) Cardinal traits _____
       Example _____
    B) Central traits _____
       Example _____
    C) Secondary traits_____
       Example _____

4. We should look at a person's _____ of central traits in order to understand that person.

## 12-7 Cattell's Factor Theory

5. Define factor analysis.

6. Describe the 2 types of traits in Cattell's theory.

7. How many traits are in Cattell's theory.

## 12-8 Eysenck's Type Theory

8. What are types, traits, and habits?

9. Define Eysenck's 3 basic bipolar dimensions.

10. People who are low in the neuroticism scale are said to _____ _____.

11. Describe Eysenck's biological basis for personality.

12.    List and describe the Big Five personality traits.

13.    Complete the table to describe the trait categories that have come to known as the *Big Five* by modern day psychologists.

| Trait Categories | Description |
|---|---|
| Extroversion-introversion | |
| | The extent to which people are good-natured or irritable, courteous or rude, flexible or stubborn, lenient or critical. |
| Conscientiousness-undirectedness | |
| Neuroticism-stability | |
| | The extent to which people are open to experience or closed, original or conventional, independent or conforming, creative or uncreative, daring or timid. |

14.    Discuss the research and findings on the genetic basis of behavior.

# Humanistic Approaches: The Search for Psychological Health

1.    Define dehumanization.

2.    What are humanistic theories?

3.    What is a phenomenological approach?

## 12-10  Maslow and Self-Actualization

4.      Describe Maslow's hierarchy of needs.


5.      What is self-actualization?


6.      Describe the self-actualized person.



## 12-11  Rogers and Self Theory

7.      What are Roger's 3 basic assumptions about human behavior?


8.      Define fulfillment.


9.      What 3 things do humans need for growth?


10.     Describe the self.


11.     The person one would ideally like to be is called the _____  _____.


12.     When does psychological stagnation occur?


13.     Describe Roger's fully-functioning person.



## 12-12  Positive Psychology

14.     What is positive psychology?


15.     Describe adaptation.


16.     What is the phenomenon of flow?

# Cognitive Approaches to Personality

**12-13  Key Cognitive Concepts**

1.    Define schema.


2.    What are self-schemata?


3.    How is the self-schema involved in personality?


**12-14  Rotter and Locus of Control**

4.    Describe locus of control.


5.    Describe people with internal locus of control and those with external locus of control.


6.    How does locus of control affect therapy?


**12-15  Bandura and Self-Efficacy**

6.    How does Bandura explain violence?


7.    Give one strategy for controlling the influence of media on violence.


8.    Define self-efficacy.


9.    How does gender impact self-efficacy?


**12-16  Mischel's Cognitive-Affective Personality System**

10.    Define interactionist.

11.    What is self-regulation?

12.    What is a cognitive-affective personality unit?

13.    Describe Mischel's 5 cognitive-affective personality units.

14.    Mischel's view of personality is different from the other views because it considers
_____ and _____.

# Personality in Cultural Context

1.    Define culture.

2.    Do cultural differences affect personality?

# Personality Assessment

| 12-17  Projective Tests |
| --- |

1.    Define assessment.

2.    What is a projective test?

3.    Describe the Rorschach Inkblot Test.

4.    What is the TAT?

| 12-18  Personality Inventories |
| --- |

5.    What is a personality inventory?

6.    Describe the MBTI.

7.    What personality inventories have been developed out of trait theory?


8.    What is the NEO-PI-R.


9.    The _____ _____ _____ is based on Maslow's humanistic
theory of personality.


10.    Describe the MMPI-2.

**Term Identification: Make flashcards for each of the following terms. Hint: Use the definitions in the margins of the chapter**

Personality
Conscious
Preconscious
Unconscious
Id
Ego
Superego
Oral Stage
Anal Stage
Phallic Stage
Oedipus Complex
Latency Stage
Genital Stage
Libido
Defense Mechanism
Repression
Fixation
Regression
Rationalization

Projection
Denial
Reaction Formation
Displacement
Sublimation
Social Interest
Collective Unconscious
Archetypes
Trait
Longitudinal Study
Type
Self-Actualization
Fulfillment
Self
Ideal Self
Self-Efficacy
Assessment
Projective Tests

# After you read . . . Self Test

## Chapter 12 Self Test

1. Which of the following *best* defines personality?(404)
   A. A collection of all behaviors an individual has ever emitted.
   B. The behaviors a person emits when he or she is with other people.
   C. Behaviors that a person emits over time and in most situations.
   D. Behaviors that make a person stand out in a crowd.

2. Freud theorized that people are energized and act the way they do because of two basic instinctual drives. They are: (410)
   A. sex and aggression.
   B. instinctual gratification and minimizing punishment.
   C. release of anxiety and tension.
   D. life and death.

3. The ego: (407)
   A. is a preconscious behavior.
   B. acts like a manager.
   C. acts like the moral branch for the id.
   D. works on the pleasure principle.

4. Georgia is very controlled in everything she does. Her desk must be neat at all times; she apologizes for the slightest hedging on someone's privacy; she cannot be spontaneous. In understanding Freud's psychosexual stages we could predict that Georgia is fixated in the                     stage. (409)
   A. oral
   B. anal
   C. phallic
   D. genital

5. Clyde has a number of extremely hostile unconscious feelings. Unknowingly, he reduces the anxiety that these feelings produce by getting involved in highly aggressive sports, such as rugby. He is using the defense mechanism known as: (411)
   A. sublimation.
   B. denial.
   C. reaction formation.
   D. projection.

6. In Freud's view of the mind, things that we are not aware of at any moment but could be aware of easily are in the _____ mind (406)
   A    preconscious
   B.   conscious
   C.   unconscious
   D.   nonconscious

7. The _____ is the personality structure that contains a person's conscience (407)
   A.   ego
   B.   superego
   C.   id
   D.   defense mechanism

8. During the oral stage of psychosexual development, the _____ is the focus of a child's primary pleasure (408)
   A.   anus
   B.   same-sex parent
   C.   opposite-sex parent
   D.   mouth

9. What is the correct order for Freud's psychosexual stages of personality development (407-408)
   A.   oral, anal, phallic, genital, latency
   B.   oral, anal, phallic, latency, genital
   C.   anal, oral, genital, latency, phallic
   D.   phallic, latency, genital, oral, anal

10. Phenomenological approaches focus on all of the following except: (424)
   A.   an individuals unique experiences with interpreting the events in the world.
   B.   examining immediate experiences rather than experiences from the past.
   C.   how people carve their own destinies through self-determination.
   D.   the therapists perception and interpretation of the clients needs.

11. Freud's psychoanalytic theory focused in two basic instincts. However, he focused mostly on sexual instincts which her termed: (410)
   A.   determinism
   B.   regression
   C.   libido
   D.   unconscious motivation

12. The defense mechanism of rationalization involves (411)
   A.   putting your own feelings unto someone else
   B.   refusing to recognize that there is any problem or anxiety
   C.   adopting behaviors that are opposite of your true feelings
   D.   thinking of a logical, rational excuse for doing what you want

13. A person who is a constant gossip yet considers everyone else a busybody, uses which defense mechanism (411)
   A. reaction formation
   B. projection
   C. sublimation
   D. repression

14. Which of the following is an example of a "type?" (420)
   A. energetic
   B. apprehensive
   C. prejudice
   D. introverted, shy, withdrawn

15. According to Allport many people do *not* have: (420)
   A. central traits.
   B. source traits.
   C. cardinal traits.
   D. secondary traits.

16. Many modern day psychologists use the *Big Five* model to understand personality because: (422)
   A. they can identify over 100,000 different traits.
   B. it provides them with a concise description of "super traits" which describes the dispositions that characterize most people.
   C. it's based on Einstein's theory of relativity.
   D. they can avoid placing personality labels on individuals.

17. According to Alfred Alder, people are motivated by feelings of _____ which leads them to strive for _____. (412)
   A. sexual desire; gratification
   B. social needs; recognition
   C. feelings of inferiority; superiority
   D. biological forces; conformity

18. Jason beats his head against the walls of his room whenever his father yells at him for not completing a household chore. From a behavioral point of view Jason's self-destructive personality is the result of: (418)
   A. early childhood experiences.
   B. a death wish.
   C. a response that has been reinforced.
   D. an overly strong libido.

19. In Jung's view, the _____ is a mystical symbol, generally circular in form that represents a person's inward striving for unity (417)
   A. mandala
   B. collective
   C. actualizer
   D. collective unconscious

237

20. According to behaviorists theorists, personality: (417)
    A.    characteristics are stable and enduring
    B.    is the sum of a person's learned tendencies
    C.    characteristics are difficult to change
    D.    has a large genetic component

21. People with an external locus of control are more likely to _____. than people with an internal locus of control. (429)
    A.    blame others for their mistakes
    B.    engage in preventative health measures
    C.    profit from psychotherapy
    D.    lose weight when they go on a diet

22. Suppose there was some aspect of your personality that you wanted to change. According to Allport, you will have the most success if this is a _____ trait of your personality (420)
    A.    central
    B.    borderline
    C.    cardinal
    D.    secondary

23. A person's belief about whether he or she can successfully engage in and execute a specific behavior is known as: (429)
    A.    self-regulation.
    B.    self-worth.
    C.    self-esteem.
    D.    self-efficacy.

24. For both men and women, research shows that their sense of self-efficacy is affected by their ability to  (431)
    A.    be independent and compete successfully
    B.    maintain good relationships with other people
    C.    fulfill social norms for the opposite gender
    D.    fulfill social norms for their own gender

25. _____ differentiated between source traits and surface traits while _____ differentiated between cardinal, central, and secondary traits.(420-421)
    A.    Carl Rogers; Gordon Allport
    B.    Gordon Allport; Raymond Cattell
    C.    Raymond Cattell; Carl Rogers
    D.    Raymond Cattell; Gordon Allport

26. Choose the best description of the id. (406)
    A.    practical and unsympathetic
    B.    irrational and selfish
    C.    devious and scheming
    D.    pragmatic and opportunistic

27. What is the primary function of the ego? (406-407)
    A.   promote behavior that is unselfish and ethical
    B.   satisfy the desires of the id in a socially acceptable way
    C.   deny and overpower the id
    D.   shift energy from the id to the superego

28. How is the Oedipus complex resolved in both sons and daughters? (409)
    A.   repression of sexual feelings
    B.   attachment to the opposite-sex parent
    C.   identification with the same-sex parent
    D.   displacement of sexual urges into substitute objects

29. Select the term used by Jung to refer to the store of images and ideas that we inherit from our ancestors and share with all human beings. (416-417)
    A.   primal representation
    B.   racial memory
    C.   psychic structure
    D.   collective unconscious

30. Hans Eysenck described personality in terms of three factors. These factors are (421)
    A.   emotional stability, extroversion, psychoticism
    B.   introversion, openness, emotional stability
    C.   emotional stability, productivity, sensitivity
    D.   openness, extroversion, psychoticism

31. Select the most basic level of Maslow's hierarchy of needs. (424)
    A.   safety needs
    B.   physiological needs
    C.   acceptance needs
    D.   esteem needs

32. A person who is irritable, rude, critical would score low on which dimension of the Big Five model of personality (422)
    A.   agreeableness
    B.   introversion
    C.   openness to experience
    D.   neuroticism

33. Mike always rationalizes his failures by blaming them on bad luck or the influence of other people. According to Rotter, he is demonstrating: (429)
    A.   low self-efficacy.
    B.   faulty encoding strategies.
    C.   negative expectancies.
    D.   an external locus of control.

34. The major focus of humanistic psychology is on each individual's motivation to (424)
    A.   defend against unconscious anxiety
    B.   overcome inferiority and achieve superiority
    C.   secure reinforcement and avoid punishement
    D.   achieve unique, personal goals

35. Select an example of a projective test of personality. (435)
    A.   Minnesota Multiphasic Personality Inventory-2
    B.   16 Personality Factor Questionnaire (16PF)
    C.   Rorschach Ink Blot Test
    D.   California Personality Inventory

36. According to Rogers, unhappiness and maladjustment result from (425)
    A.   anxiety that is created by unconscious impulses
    B.   our inability to overcome our sense of inadequecy
    C.   discrepancies between the real self and the ideal self
    D.   the conditioning of inappropriate behavior

37. Rogers believed that _____ is an inborn tendency directing people toward self-actualization. (425)
    A.   fulfillment
    B.   idealization
    C.   conditional regard
    D.   phenomenology

38. The Oedipus conflict arises and must be resolved during the _____ stage of psychosexual development. (409)
    A.   genital
    B.   phallic
    C.   anal
    D.   oral

39. Self-determination is most closely associated with which of the following theories? (424)
    A.   psycholanalyitc
    B.   trait
    C.   humanistic
    D.   behavioral

40. A stable defining feature of an individual's personality is a: (420)
    A.   factor
    B.   self-concept
    C.   type
    D.   trait

41. A key concept in cognitive theories of personality is the self-schema, which is (427)
    A.   our repressed, unconscious impulses
    B.   our beliefs and understandings about ourselves
    C.   the archetypes in our personal unconscious
    D.   the history of our classical and operant conditioning

42. According to Rotter, our locus of control is (428)
    A.   whether we control out own lives, or are controlled by outside forces
    B.   how much we try to control the behavior of other people who are important to us
    C.   whether we direct our efforts at control toward people above or below us
    D.   how many people we have under our direct or indirect control

43. According to Mischel, we base out responses on our past experiences and our assessment of the present situation, in a process he calls (431)
    A.   internalization
    B.   behavior modification
    C.   self-regulation
    D.   reaction formation

44. Paula was asked to interpret a blob of color while a psychologist analyzed her answers Paula is taking what type of personality test? (435)
    A.   Rorschach Inkblot test
    B.   Stochastic Modeling test
    C.   Thematic Apperception Test
    D.   MMPI

45. The _____ is one of the most widely used and best-researched personality tests (437)
    A.   16PF
    B.   CPI
    C.   MMPI-2
    D.   LOR

# When You Have Finished

## Essay Questions:

1.    What are the criticisms of Freud's theory? (413)

2.    What is Skinner's approach to personality formation?(417-418)

3.    In terms of Roger's theory, what is locus of control and how does it affect personality?(428-429)

4.    What is the focus and emphasis of positive psychology and what does their research on happiness indicate? (426)

5.    Different cultures have the same Five Factor Model structure, explain why this does not mean people of different cultures have the same personality (433-434)

# Chapter 13

# Social Psychology

# Before you read...

Social psychologists are interested in how individuals influence and are influenced by the thoughts, feelings, and behavior of others. Attitudes are expressed through either cognitive, emotional, or behavioral dimensions. Although behavior is not always predicted by attitudes, the presence of four variables increase the likelihood of this occurring. The four variables are attitude strength, vested interest, specificity of the attitude, and accessibility of attitudes.

Changing people's attitudes requires four components: the communicator must project integrity, credibility, and trustworthiness; the communication should be clear, convincing, and logical; the medium usually requires face-to-face communication; and the audience is susceptible to change. Petty and Cacioppo offer the elaboration-likelihood model for attitude change, which consists of two routes for changing attitudes. The central route relies on effective, authoritative, and logical communication, and the peripheral route is more indirect and relies more on the delivery and the communicator. Lefton and Brannon outline several techniques to induce attitude change. Attitudes change throughout life primarily because we generally search for cognitive consistency. Cognitive dissonance, self-perception theory, and reactance theory offer explanations of how we strive for these consistencies.

Many personal interactions rely on social cognition which attempts to understand other people's communications to form impressions of them. This process can be verbal or nonverbal, and we tend to create mental shortcuts to facilitate impression formation. A modest amount of eye contact leaves the most lasting impression and conveys a surprising amount of information.

Making an attribution involves inferring someone's motives and intentions by observing their behavior and determining whether that behavior is dispositional or situational. We rely on consensus, consistency, and distinctiveness to determine whether the causes of the behavior are internal or external. The two most common attribution errors are the fundamental attribution error and the actor-observer effect. Errors in self attribution can lead to self-serving bias.

The next section in the text explores prejudice and how it can be prevented. When prejudice translates into behavior it is called discrimination. Four theories are considered in explaining prejudice: social learning theory, motivational theory, cognitive theory, and personality theory. To reduce and eliminate prejudice we must begin to think of people as individuals, not as members of a group.

The next section of the text looks at social influence and focuses on conformity and obedience. Asch's studies on conformity found that people adopt a group standard even when they are not pressured to do so. Four variables interact to produce conformity. They are social conformity, attribution, risks of independence, and expediency. Additionally, Milgram's studies of obedience provide understanding into when people will conform and obey.

Our behavior in groups differs somewhat from our independent behaviors. Social facilitation theory asserts that our behavior is affected not only by membership in a group but also by the presence of a group. Social loafing suggests that individual performance and effort decline when working in a group. We make decisions that may be riskier when we are subject to group influence. This is called group polarization. In another light, people in a group seeking concurrence with one another tend to make premature decisions in the interest of getting along, by a method called groupthink. Finally, unrestricted group behavior such as mob violence is examined from the perspective of deindividuation.

The old theory that people are innately aggressive is wrong. We now know that aggression can be learned and is usually displayed when we feel unable to control situations. Exposure to violence is also shown to weaken inhibitions, suggest techniques, stimulate aggressive ideas, and reduce a person's overall emotional sensitivity to violence. Men are more physically aggressive, but both men and women use psychological aggression. Lefton and Brannon conclude this section with a look at domestic violence.

Is prosocial behavior like altruism learned or inherited? Behaviorists contend that prosocial behavior is self-reinforcing and therefore can become a powerful initiator of prosocial behavior. On the other hand, sociobiologists suggest that prosocial behavior is simply an inherited tendency to survive. Latane' and Darley offer an explanation for bystander apathy.

Attraction to others and the formation of relationships depend on several factors. Proximity, physical attractiveness, and shared interests and attitudes contribute to relationships. Friendship is a two-way interaction, and equity plays an important role in friendships. Intimacy and love are discussed as special relationships. The central components of love appear to be intimacy, commitment, and passion.

# Chapter Objectives

- Characterize the field of social psychology; then describe the three dimensions of an attitude and explain how attitudes and convictions can guide behavior.

- List and describe the four key attitudinal variables that are said to predict behavior.

- Identify the four components of attitude change and describe the elaboration-likelihood model used to explain the cognitions of individuals whose attitudes are being changed.

- Explain why people seek to maintain consistency between their attitudes and their behavior, and describe how they try to maintain consistency according to cognitive dissonance, self-perception, and reactance theories.

- Describe six techniques to induce attitude change.

- Describe the thought process of social cognition, and its relation to impression formation.

- Describe how mental short cuts help people process information and decrease information overload.

- Discuss the three major means of nonverbal communication by which people convey information about their moods and attitudes.

- Explain how people infer the motives and intentions of others through the process of attribution, discuss the three criteria people use to determine whether the causes of a behavior are internal or external, and describe two common attribution errors and how they obscure the real motives and intentions of people's behavior.

- Define *prejudice* and *discrimination*, summarize the four theoretical explanations of the causes of prejudice, and list several ways people can work toward reducing and eliminating prejudice

- Explain how social influence arises from conformity and obedience and evaluate the methods, results, and important conclusions of the classic studies by Asch and Milgram.

- Define *social facilitation*; then describe the concepts of social loafing, group polarization, groupthink, and deindividuation and their effects on behavior in groups.

- Discuss the influence television has on aggressive and prosocial behaviors.

- Review the sociobiological explanations of prosocial behaviors such as altruism.

- Discuss how proximity, physical attractiveness, and shared attitudes contribute to interpersonal attraction and list some common elements found in love relationships.

# As you read...

## Attitudes: Deeply Held Feelings and Beliefs

1. Define Social Psychology

2. What is an attitude?

---

**13-1    Dimensions and Functions of Attitudes**

1. List and describe the 3 dimensions of attitudes.

2. The _____ dimension of an attitude involves evaluative feelings, such as like and dislike.

3. Since people become identified with their strong attitudes, attitudes are _____ and _____ to change.

---

**13-2    Do Attitudes Predict Behavior?**

1. Describe 4 variables of attitudes that affect their predictability of behavior.

2. If a believe is also part of a person's _____then it is a good predictor of behavior.

3. Behaviors are not predicted well by _____ attitudes.

---

**13-3    Does Behavior Determine Attitudes?**

1. Describe the Stanford Prison Experiment.

2. What does the Stanford Prison Experiment tell us about attitudes and behavior?

## 13-4    Persuasion: Changing Attitudes

1. Describe Hovland's 4 key components of attitude change.

2. What 3 things must a communicator project to change attitudes?

3. A communication needs to be _____, _____ and
   _____, to be an effectively change attitudes.

4. What is the mere exposure effect?

5. The way in which communication is presented, its _____, influences people's
   receptiveness to new ideas.

6. List some aspects of the audience that influence attitude change.

## 13-5    Tactics and Techniques for Inducing Attitude Change

1. Describe the foot-in-the-door technique.

2. What is the door-in-the-face technique?

3. Describe the ask-and-you-shall –be-given technique.

4. What is lowballing?

5. Describe modeling.

6. Define the incentive technique.

7. Do we listen to what "they" say?

---

**13-6   The Elaboration Likelihood Model**

---

1. Define the Elaboration Likelihood Model.

2. What is the central route?

3. Describe the peripheral route.

4. When is each route used?

---

**13-7   Searching for Cognitive Consistency**

---

1. Define consistency.

2. What is cognitive dissonance?

3. According to the _____ _____ theory, people feel compelled to change their attitudes or their behaviors when there is a conflict between them.

4. What is the self-perception theory?

5. When people feel their freedoms are restricted, they often react negatively and try to reestablish their freedom. This negative influence is known as _____.

# Social Cognition: The Impact of Thought

1. What is social cognition?

2. Define impression formation.

## 13-8 Organizing the World Using Mental Shortcuts

1. What is a cognitive miser?

2. What are the 4 rules of thumb people develop to help them make decisions?

3. Sometimes people have a tendency to believe that others believe exactly what they believe to be true. This rule of thumb is known as _____ _____ _____.

4. The way people present or _____ information helps others to process it and accept it easily.

## 13-9 Assessing the World Using Nonverbal Communication

1. What is nonverbal communication?

2. How do facial expressions influence communication?

3. Define body language.

4. Describe the importance of eye contact in nonverbal communication.

## 13-10 Inferring the Causes of Behavior: Attribution

1. Define attribution.

2. What are internal and external attributions?

3. List and describe the 3 criteria people use to decide if a behavior is caused by internal or external factors.

4. In the table below, Kelly's criteria for determining whether the causes of a behavior are due to internal characteristics of an individual or to external factors is presented. Kelly's criteria for internal vs. external attribution are based on consensus, consistency, and distinctiveness.

INTERNAL

1. _____ _____:
_____ others act the same way.

2. _____ _____: Person acts the same way in other _____ situations.

3. _____ _____:
Person acts in the same way on other occasions.

EXTERNAL

1. _____ _____:
_____ act the _____ way.

2. _____ _____:
Person acts the same way in other _____ situations.

3. _____ _____:
Person acts differently in other situations.

5. What purpose do attributions serve?

6. What is the fundamental attribution error?

7. Define the actor-observer effect.

8. Describe the self-serving bias.

## 13-11  Prejudice

1. Define prejudice.

2. What is a stereotype?

3. Define discrimination.

4. A person who is prejudice but does not show discrimination is referred to as a _____ _____.

5. What is reverse discrimination?

6. Describe tokenism.

7. Describe how social learning theory, motivational theory, cognitive theory and personality theory explain prejudice?

8. What is an illusionary correlation?

9. Define social categorization.

10. Describe the authoritarian personality.

11. Define symbolic racism.

12. What is racial resentment?

13. How can racism be reduced?

# Social Interactions

### 13-12 Social Influence

1. Define social influence.

2. What is conformity?

3. Describe Ashe's research on social conformity.

4. List and describe 4 variables that effect conformity.

5. Describe the social conformity approach.

6. How do dissenting opinions impact conformity?

7. Compliance with the orders of others is called _____.

8. Describe Milgram's study.

9. What is background authority?

10. What is the purpose of a debriefing?

## 13-13  Groups: Sharing Common Goals

1. Define group.

2. What is social facilitation?

3. When _____ _____ occurs a person's effort and productivity decreases as the result of working in a group.

4. What things increase and decrease social loafing?

5. What is group polarization?

6. Define choice shift.

7. Describe persuasive argument.

8.  What is diffusion of responsibility?

9.  How does social comparison impact group polarization?

10. Describe group think.

11. Describe 2 things that can lead to unrestrained group behavior?

---

**13-14  Aggression and Violence: The Threatening Side of Human Behavior**

1.  Define aggression.

2.  What is the frustration-aggression hypothesis?

3.  How does cognitive psychology explain violence and aggression?

4.  _____ to a person's self-esteem can cause aggression.

5.  Describe the excitation transfer theory.

6.  What does research reveal about television and violence?

7.  What key effects of viewing violence on television does Smith describe?

8.  Do rating systems work?

9.  What Genders differences exist in aggression?

10. Describe the biological bases of aggression.

## 13-15  Prosocial Behavior

1.  Define prosocial behavior.

2.  A behavior that is had no rewards is considered _____.

3.  How do behaviorists explain prosocial behavior?

4.  What is sociobiology?

5.  What is the bystander effect?

6.  Under what conditions are bystanders more likely to help?

## 13-16  Relationships and Attraction

1.  Define interpersonal attraction.

2.  Describe proximity and physical attractiveness and their relationship to interpersonal attraction.

3.  How does similarity affect relationship development?

4.  Define friendship.

5.  What is equity theory?

6.  Define intimacy.

7.  List the 4 different definitions of love.

8. Compare and contrast passionate and companionate love.

9. List Sternberg's 3 components of love.

10. What is an ex post facto design?

11. Describe Field's research and conclusions.

12. Describe the cultural difference in love.

| 13-17   **Evolution and Social Psychology** |

1. How do evolutionists view social behavior?

2. How do the evolutionists view attraction?

**Term Identification: Make flashcards for each of the following terms. Hint: Use the definitions in the margins of the chapter**

Social Psychology
Attitudes
Elaboration Likelihood Model
Cognitive Dissonance
Self-Perception Theory
Reactance
Social Cognition
Impression Formation
Nonverbal Communication
Body Language
Attribution
Fundamental Attribution Error
Actor-Observer Effect
Self-Serving Bias
Prejudice
Stereotypes
Discrimination
Social Categorization
Social Influence

Conformity
Obedience
Debriefing
Group
Social Facilitation
Social Loafing
Group Polarization
Groupthink
Deindividuation
Aggression
Prosocial Behavior
Altruism
Sociobiology
Bystander Effect
Interpersonal Attraction
Equity Theory
Ex Post Facto Design
Intimacy

# After you read . . . Self Test

## Chapter 13 Self Test

1. Which of the following is *not* of major concern to social psychology? (442)
   A. How and why people establish cultures.
   B. Why people sometimes use the standards of others to measure their own feelings of self-worth.
   C. How one adult can influence the behavior of another adult.
   D. How to minimize or maximize the factors that affect behavior that are present when two or more people are together.

2. Which of the following is the *behavioral* component of the attitude that children should be respected as human beings? (443)
   A. Believing that children are worthy of all the respect you would give to an adult.
   B. Feeling very upset if you see the rights of a child infringed upon by an adult.
   C. Acknowledging a child for holding his or her own opinion about a social issue even if it differs from your own.
   D. Having a sense of elation when you read about a child who is a computer wizard and has started his or her own business.

3. Attitudes: (442-443)
   A. may or may not be displayed in overt, public behavior.
   B. when combined with one's perception of the environment, determine behavior.
   C. are determined by experience.
   D. all of the above

4. Attitudes are composed of three dimensions, which are (443)
   A. conscious, unconscious, and preconscious
   B. cognitive, emotional, and behavioral
   C. internal, external, and conditional
   D. primary, secondary, and tertiary

5. Which of the following is *not* true? Psychologists feel fairly confident about predicting the behavior of an individual if they know his/her attitude about something and: (443-444)
   A. a decision that closely matches the attitude needs to be made.
   B. there are few competing forces, and the attitude is strongly held by the individual.
   C. the individual has described the attitude-behavior sequence.
   D. the attitude was established through personal experience.

6. Which of the following does *not* tend to contribute to a speaker's effectiveness in promoting attitude change? (445)
   A. The speaker is attractive.
   B. The audience believes the speaker is powerful and prestigious.
   C. The speaker is able to surprise the audience with new and unexpected ideas.
   D. The speaker uses a layman's vocabulary when speaking to people not closely related to his or her own field.

7. According to Petty and Cacioppo, peripheral processes involved in attitude change: (449)
   A. lead to rational decisions.
   B. allow a person to attend to how logical a communication actually is.
   C. have an indirect, but powerful effect.
   D. all of the above

8. That people will begin to think positively about a persuasive message if they hear is repeatedly is called (445)
   A. low balling
   B. persuasive appeal
   C. the foot-in-the-door technique
   D. the mere exposure effect

9. According to the self-perception view put forth by Bem, the situations individuals find themselves in lead to: (450)
   A. the experience of dissonance and ultimately decisions that will influence their future behavior.
   B. inferences concerning their emotions, attitudes and the causes of their behaviors.
   C. paying attention to the reinforcements and punishments associated with change.
   D. establishing friendships that allow them to maintain a consistency in their belief systems.

10. If Barb's mother tells Barb that she has to go to college, and Barb responds by moving out of the house, taking a full-time job in a restaurant, and spending her free time doing aerobic exercises, *reactance theory* would suggest that Barb: (451)
    A. has a rebellious attitude.
    B. needed to maintain consistency with her beliefs and behaviors.
    C. behaved as she did in order to maintain a sense of autonomy.
    D. was not open to parental advice or suggestions.

11. The effects of gender on nonverbal communication are apparent in the observation that: (453)
    A. men are better than women at interpreting facial expressions.
    B. women are more cautious than men in interpreting nonverbal messages from the opposite sex.
    C. men are more likely than women to send nonverbal facial messages.
    D. all of the above

12. When psychologists examine the internal motivations for a person's behavior they: (453)
    A.    focus on behavioral genetics.
    B.    must look at behaviors that have only one cause.
    C.    decide whether to attribute the behavior to internal or external causes.
    D.    ask the person to give an evaluation of his or her own behavior.

13. According to Kelly, we attribute behavior to *internal* causes when we evaluate a behavior and situation and find: (454)
    A.    low consensus, consistency, and distinctiveness.
    B.    high consensus, consistency, and distinctiveness.
    C.    low consensus and distinctiveness, with high consistency.
    D.    high consensus and distinctiveness, with low consistency.

14. When Carolyn walked in the door, home late from work, Steve lost his temper. According to attribution studies: (455)
    A.    Steve will explain his behavior by reference to some situational factor such as his concern that the company would show up before his wife did.
    B.    Carolyn will explain his behavior by reference to some internal characteristic such as Steve is too dependent.
    C.    Steve and Carolyn will realize that the world is not always a just world.
    D.    A and B

15. Which of these is an example of how someone who is using the foot-in-the-door technique to get a friend to look after his dog for a week might begin? (447)
    A.    "Will you loan me $1000 for my dog's surgery?"
    B.    "Could you watch my dog for one afternoon?"
    C.    "Would you please look after my dog for a week?"
    D.    "I'll look after your three cats this summer in return."

16. The Stanford Prison Experiment showed that: (444)
    A.    attitudes influence and shape behavior
    B.    changes in attitude may follow from a set of behaviors
    C.    the elaboration likelihood model is an accurate model of attitude formation and attitude change
    D.    role-playing plays only a minor role in the formation and changing of attitudes

17. An unpleasant experience that results from a conflict between two different attitudes or between attitudes and behavior is called (449)
    A.    social incentives
    B.    elaboration likelihood
    C.    frustration aggression
    D.    cognitive dissonance.

18. Which of the following is a good example of a self-serving bias? (455)
    A.  Bryant wants a better job so he looks for and finds one.
    B.  Ted has had four accidents in three months and he tells Sue that he really is one of the best drivers around.
    C.  Rayna sees Alex slip something under the bed and decides that he is hiding something from her.
    D.  Sheila buys a new outfit so that she can look terrific for her new love.

19. The thought processes we use to understand and remember information about other people and our interactions with them is called (451)
    A.  elaboration likelihood method
    B.  cognitive dissonance theory
    C.  group polarization
    D.  social cognition

20. Solomon Asch's conformity/line discrimination experiment: (462-463)
    A.  made use of collaborators who actively pressured a naive subject.
    B.  involved a fairly difficult task of distinguishing between two lines of almost equal length.
    C.  involved deception.
    D.  all of the above

21. In Asch's experiment the naive subject gave a correct answer concerning the length of the lines: (463)
    A.  about fifty percent of the time.
    B.  even when the ten collaborators gave the incorrect answer.
    C.  when one out of ten collaborators gave the correct answer.
    D.  none of the above

22. Dissenting opinions within a group: (463)
    A.  generally strengthen the group's influence upon individuals.
    B.  can have a substantial influence on the decision making of a large group even if only two people are dissenting.
    C.  become influential only when a majority of the members agree with the opposition.
    D.  do not influence the group unless they come from a consistent minority that holds power and is considered highly competent.

23. Which of the following is most likely to enhance a group's ability to exert pressure upon an individual? (463)
    A.  a small group of two or three members
    B.  a group that requires public statements of opinion
    C.  individuals who feel they are competent to make decisions on their own
    D.  groups that deal with unambiguous issues

24. Which of the following does not provide an explanation for why people conform? (463)
    A. Through attribution processes an individual is able to identify causes for the behavior of people in the group.
    B. People want to do whatever is generally accepted as "right."
    C. The risks of being independent are high.
    D. People want to avoid the stigma of being different or deviant.

25. The rule of thumb called availability implies that we are more likely to use a category or idea to describe something if the category or idea is (452)
    A. easier to bring to mind
    B. more pleasant
    C. more unpleasant
    D. classically conditioned

26. Debriefing: (466)
    A. is a necessary feature in many experiments investigating social psychology issues.
    B. enables a researcher to conduct an experiment that might otherwise be considered unethical.
    C. enables a researcher to conduct an experiment that will provide valid unbiased responses.
    D. all of the above

27. What branch of psychology focuses on the influences that other people have on our thoughts and behaviors? (442)
    A. social
    B. developmental
    C. clinical
    D. personality

28. _____ - holds that people learn their prejudices through first observing those prejudices in others and then being rewarded for holding or acting on those prejudices (458)
    A. Personality theory
    B. Cognitive theory
    C. Motivation theory
    D. Social learning theory

29. Kim's arguments are logical and convincing. What persuasion route should she use in order to be better able to produce attitude change in her audience? (449)
    A. heuristic
    B. central
    C. peripheral
    D. elaborative

30. Who is associated with the self-perception theory? (450)
    A. Stanley Milgram
    B. Solomon Asch
    C. Leon Festinger
    D. Daryl Bem

31. In what way do TV advertisers indicate awareness of the reactance phenomenon? (451)
    A. emphasize that the buyer has a choice
    B. are careful in their criticism of competing products
    C. use messages that make the audience feel good about themselves
    D. limit the amount of information in commercials

32. Name the process that people use to infer the internal states and intentions of others from their behavior and appearance. (451)
    A. social interpretation
    B. interpersonal perception
    C. impression formation
    D. social facilitation

33. When are people more likely to conform?(463)
    A. if they have an internal locus of control
    B. if they are confident that they have high status in the group
    C. when the group is small
    D. when the situation is ambiguous

34. The most updated version of the frustration-aggression hypothesis suggests that: (471)
    A. when goal-directed behavior is interrupted people will become aggressive.
    B. frustration may cause a variety of responses.
    C. frustration creates a readiness for aggression and is more likely to lead to aggressive acts if certain circumstances are present.
    D. B and C

35. Which of the following statements concerning research investigating television's relationship to aggressive behavior is *false*? (473)
    A. People who observe TV violence are more likely to intervene and help victims of real violence.
    B. Most studies show that TV violence increases the incidence of real-life violence.
    C. Aggressive children tend to watch more television than nonaggressive children.
    D. Television can be beneficial in establishing positive social and personal behaviors.

36. Which statement describes prejudice and discrimination? (457)
    A. Prejudice and discrimination are both emotional states.
    B. Reverse discrimination is when a bigot is treated with prejudice and discrimination.
    C. Prejudice is an attitude and discrimination is a behavior.
    D. People who are prejudiced, but do not discriminate, are called non-discriminatory bigots.

37. According to scientific evidence, you are most likely to be attracted to: (479)
    A.   your neighbors and work associates.
    B.   people you have met only once.
    C.   people you have met and have difficulty visiting often.
    D.   people who have ideas very different from your own.

38. When it comes to liking someone, people tend to: (481)
    A.   keep a distance until they have evidence about the person they like.
    B.   assume that the person they like is like them and likes them.
    C.   almost always choose people who have personalities very similar to their own.
    D.   seek friends who are less attractive and socially skilled than they perceive themselves to be.

39. Physical attractiveness seems to play a role in attraction: (479-480)
    A.   only in our youth-oriented culture.
    B.   in the Western world, but not in primitive and agricultural societies.
    C.   at least at first.
    D.   to men in all cultures, but not to women in all cultures.

40. People are motivated to feel attracted to those they believe share similar attitudes in order to: (481)
    A.   avoid cognitive dissonance.
    B.   guarantee equity.
    C.   have something to talk about.
    D.   experience a sense of love.

41. What is meant by the term "social facilitation?" (466)
    A.   negative effects on one's performance due to the presence of others
    B.   both positive and negative effects on one's performance due to the presence of others
    C.   positive effects on one's performance due to the presence of others
    D.   none of the above
    E.

42. Choose the best definition of prejudice. (457)
    A.   a negative evaluation of an entire group of people
    B.   behavior that treats people differently because of race, religion, or color
    C.   the attribution of personality traits on the basis of perceived group membership
    D.   the belief that one's own group is superior to all other groups

43. Randy helped a homeless family because he would be featured in the newspaper. His behavior was motivated largely by personal rewards. Larry helped a homeless family because he was concerned for their welfare. What motivated Larry's behavior? (476)
    A.   egoism
    B.   bystander apathy
    C.   sociobiology
    D.   altruism

44. What concept has been used by behaviorists to explain altruism? (477)
    A.  intermittent reinforcement
    B.  stimulus generalization
    C.  intrinsic rewards
    D.  successive approximation

45. Which theory says that people attempt to maintain interpersonal relationships in which the ratio of costs and benefits are equal for both parties? (481)
    A.  social exchange
    B.  group balance
    C.  equity
    D.  justice motive

# When You Have Finished

## Essay Questions:

1. What is the fundamental attribution error and why is it made. (455)

2. How can social conformity be achieved? (463)

3. Explain how the bystander effect and diffusion of responsibility cause people not to help others. (477-479)

4. Compare and contrast the motivational theory and cognitive theory of prejudice (458-459)

5. What is social loafing, when does it occur and how can it be minimized?(467-468)

# Chapter 14

# Stress and Health Psychology

## Before you read...

This chapter presents a contemporary view of stress, coping, and the field of health psychology. It begins by defining stress and stressors. A stressor is an environmental stimulus that has the potential to affect an organism in a harmful way by producing anxiety or tension. Stress is the end result of that stimulus. The key is the interpretation of the stressor as being stressful. Sources of stress include frustration, conflict, and pressure. Responses to stress include emotional, physical, and behavioral reactions. While a moderate amount of stress is thought to be adaptive, too much may lead to burnout, a state of physical and emotional exhaustion, which contribute to serious health problems such as heart disease and cancer by affecting the body's immune system.

Hans Selye developed a model describing physiological changes resulting from stress. He called this model the general adaptation syndrome. The syndrome consists of three stages: the alarm stage, the resistance stage, and finally exhaustion. Holmes and Rahe developed a scale to assess the potential for a stress-induced illness following a series of life events. Work-site stress, Type A behavior, and physiological reactivity are examined for their relationships to heart disease. Victims of war, crime, natural disasters, and man-made disasters have the potential to suffer from posttraumatic stress disorder (PTSD). Although most of the research on PTSD is with war veterans, many organizations and practitioners are using this knowledge to mitigate the effects of PTSD through early intervention techniques with other populations of victims.

Deal with it! This is one way of defining coping. Our ability to cope depends on a number of factors including our resilience, current coping skills, and social supports. We may choose defense-oriented or task-oriented coping strategies. Defense-oriented strategies isolate the stress, but do not provide long term solutions. Task-oriented strategies clearly identify the source of stress, develop a plan of action, and through implementation and monitoring usually results in effective change.

Health psychology is an emerging field that looks to incorporate the principles of health enhancement, prevention, diagnosis, and rehabilitation into a more holistic approach. Our personality, thoughts, social environment, and sociocultural variables all contribute to good health. *Psychology* examines how psychologists are addressing the AIDS issue from a behavioral perspective. Psychologists are looking more closely at the "psychology of being sick" and how education and prevention can be used to help people become and remain healthy.

# Chapter Objectives

- Characterize stress, and indicate the importance of cognitive appraisal in the determination of what is stressful.
- Identify the three stages of Selye's general adaptation syndrome, and describe the Holmes-Rahe Social Readjustment Rating Scale.
- Understand Lazarus's view of stress and cognitive appraisal.
- Describe the three broad sources of stress, and state how the work environment and life events can contribute to stress.
- Identify the origins and symptoms of posttraumatic stress disorder.
- Describe some of the physical, emotional, and behavioral responses that people can have when they are under stress; and identify some of the health consequences and ethnic differences in response to stressors.
- Summarize what is currently known about the relationship between stress and heart disease.
- Define what is meant by the term *coping* and outline the relationship among resilience, coping skills, social support, and ability to cope.
- Distinguish between emotion-focused and problem-focused coping strategies, and outline a plan for developing a stress reduction program.
- Assess how positive and negative attitudes influence coping abilities and the immune system, and state steps one can take to develop effective coping strategies.
- Describe the fields of health psychology and behavioral medicine and explain what contemporary psychologists mean by the term *health*.
- Discuss how personality, cognition, social environment, gender, and sociocultural variables are related to health.
- Describe how health psychologists involved in AIDS prevention are educating the public about high-risk behaviors.
- Explain what is meant by the psychology of being sick, focusing on when people seek medical care and adopt a sick role and under what circumstances they may comply with medical advice.
- Explain how behavioral interventions, pain management, and stress management try to develop adaptive behaviors that will improve people's lives.

# As you read...

## Stress

1.      Define stress.

2.      What is a stressor?

3.      Describe General Adaptation Syndrome.

4.      A set of responses is a _____.

5.      List and describe Selye's 3 stages of stress response?

6.      What are Stressful life events?

7.      Describe the Social Readjustment Rating Scale.

8.      Describe the Undergraduate Stress Questionnaire.

9.      Define cognitive appraisal.

10.     What 3 things influence a person's cognitive appraisal?

11.     What are the Hassles Scales?

14-2    Sources of Stress

12.     What are catastrophes?

13. Describe PTSD.

14.. How did Psychologists try to help after September 11?

15. List some environmental factors in stress.

16. What is urban press?

17. How does discrimination lead to stress?

18. Define reactivity

19. What is an experimental design

20. Describe the conclusions of Fang and Myer's experiment.

21. Describe factors leading to work stress and relationship stress

| 14-3 | **Responses to Stress** |
|---|---|

22. Describe the physiological response to stress.

23. The adrenal glands release the hormones _____ and _____ in response to stress.

24. What is the role of cortisol in the stress response?

25. Describe the behavioral response to stress.

26.     Describe heart disease.

27.     Describe Type A and Type B behavior.

28.     What behaviors and attitudes are linked with heart disease?

29.     How is stress related to infectious diseases?

30.     Define immunity.

31.     What is psychoneuroimmunology.

32.     Can the immune system be conditioned?

33.     What are cytokins?

34.     What 3 factors of stress are important in vulnerability to infection?

35.     How does stress impact health related behaviors?

# Coping

**14-5 What is Coping?**

1.      Define coping.

2.      List the 5 assumptions of coping.

3.      Define resilience.

4.      List and describe 3 factors that influence coping.

5.      People who have the _____ of control show health benefits.

6.      What is learned helplessness?

7.      What is the importance of social support?

14-7   **Coping Strategies**

8.      Define coping strategies.

9.      Typically _____ coping strategies are more effective than _____ coping strategies.

10.     Describe the two types of active coping strategies.

11.     List 3 types of emotion-focused coping strategies.

12.     What is proactive coping?

13.     What are the 5 stages of proactive coping?

14.     Describe stress inoculation.

# Health Psychology

15.    Define health psychology.

16.    List 5 behaviors correlated with health and life expectancy.

17.    Give examples of health-impairing behaviors.

18.    List the high-risk behaviors involved in getting AIDS.

19.    Describe optimistic bias.

14-9    The Psychology of Being Sick

20.    What are some factors that make people more likely to seek medical care?

21.    Describe gender differences in seeking medical care.

22.    What cultural differences exist in seeking medical care?

23.    What is the main reason people seek alternative medicine?

24.    What type of people seek alternative medicine?

25.    Describe the sick role.

26.    When are people more likely to comply with medical advice?

27. Describe the 3 forms severe pain can take.

28. How does behavior modification work in pain management?

29. What are workplace wellness programs

30. Define community intervention.

31. Describe the safe sex campaign.

**14-11 Health Psychology and the Future**

32. What factors contribute to wellness?

33. Describe the integration involved in health psychology.

**Term Identification: Make flashcards for each of the following terms.
Hint: Use the definitions in the margins of the chapter**

Burnout
Stress
Stressor
Post Traumatic Stress Disorder
Type A Behavior
Type B Behavior
Psychoneuroimmunology

Coping
Resilience
Coping Strategies
Social Support
Stress Inoculation
Proactive Coping
Health Psychology

# After you read . . . Self Test

## Chapter 14 Self Test

1. An environmental stimulus that affects an organism in physically or psychologically injurious ways is called: (491)
    - A. a stressor.
    - B. stress.
    - C. anxiety.
    - D. arousal.

2. Children often show their stress response: (501)
    - A. by laughing.
    - B. by telling their teachers and parents about their discomfort.
    - C. with symptoms of physical illness.
    - D. by playing a game of charades.

3. Which of the following would be classified as a high stress job? (500)
    - A. air traffic controllers
    - B. inner-city high school teacher
    - C. customer service agent
    - D. all of the above

4. A physiological response to stress is characterized by arousal of the _____ nervous system. (501)
    - A. central
    - B. somatic
    - C. autonomic
    - D. bilateral

5. Cosmos has very high standards in accomplishing the tasks at his job. However, because of extreme work related pressures, he has been experiencing emotional and physical exhaustion lower productivity, and has felt isolated from the other employees. Cosmos is experiencing: (490)
    - A. reality.
    - B. burnout.
    - C. anxiety.
    - D. resistance

6. At this stage of Selye's GAS, physiological and behavioral responses become more moderate and sustained. (492)
    - A. alarm
    - B. acceptance
    - C. resistance
    - D. exhaustion

7. According to Holmes and Rahe, stressful life events are: (493)
   A. every day hassles in a person's day-to-day experiences.
   B. a combination of every day hassles and irritations.
   C. the build up of every day hassles and irritations.
   D. prominent events in a person's life that necessitate change.

8. Type A behavior (504)
   A. does not seem directly related to heart disease
   B. is marked by decreases physiological reactivity
   C. is marked by competitiveness, happiness and patience
   D. causes heart disease

9. Which of the following events contribute to post traumatic stress disorder? (497)
   A. victims of violence
   B. natural disasters
   C. man-made disasters
   D. all of the above

10. Someone who is resilient is someone who responds to demanding situations by (507-508)
    A. triggering a powerful defense mechanism
    B. reducing their level of immune system functioning
    C. exhibiting a high level of physiological reactance
    D. taking them in stride and dealing with them

11. The availability of comfort, recognition, approval, and encouragement from other people is called _____ and is extremely helpful when people are trying to cope. (509)
    A. psychological manipulation
    B. social support
    C. friendship
    D. mentoring

12. Taking steps to prevent a stressful event from occurring is an example of (511)
    A. defense-oriented coping
    B. emotion-focused coping
    C. proactive cooping
    D. anticipatory coping

13. The study of how psychological processes and the nervous system affect and are affected by the immune system is called (505)
    A. pscyhobiology
    B. psychoneuroimmunology
    C. biopsychology
    D. psychoimmunology

14. With respect to AIDS, a high-risk behavior is on that (515)
    A. exposes one to the blood or semen of someone who might have AIDS
    B. brings one into any contact, even casual, with an AIDS sufferer
    C. increases the likelihood of dying from the disease
    D. makes the symptoms of the disease more serious

15. In general, people are more likely to seek medical care when (516)
    A.   they are men
    B.   their problem is psychological
    C.   they believe their condition is curable
    D.   they have visible symptoms

16.  A narrow subfield of health psychology that emphasizes the application of behavioral science to medical knowledge and treatments is called (513)
    A.   genetic engineering
    B.   behavioral medicine
    C.   medical conditioning
    D.   internal medicine

17. Someone who suspects that he or she might have a very serious, life-threatening illness for which there may be no cure is very likely to (516)
    A.   seek medical care immediately
    B.   engage in behavioral stress reduction
    C.   switch to preventive medical treatments
    D.   delay or avoid seeking medical care

18. Cognitive appraisal is a process by which people (493)
    A.   develop emotional reactions to environmental events
    B.   assess how successful they have been in the past
    C.   evaluate a situation and their ability to deal with it
    D.   try out various stress reduction strategies

19. If we feel have control over something that happens, in general that makes it(494-495)
    A.   our responsibility, so it is more stressful
    B.   less interesting and challenging to us
    C.   harder to ignore and harder to deal with
    D.   more predictable and less stressful

20. People are *less* likely to comply when: (519)
    A.   advice is for wellness or prevention.
    B.   when family and friends pressure the patient.
    C.   an illness is chronic.
    D.   they have no fears of the possible diagnosis.

21. Pain which is long-lasting and ever-present is: (520)
    A.   chronic pain.
    B.   periodic pain.
    C.   progressive pain.
    D.   accute pain.

22. Which of these factors seems to be most strongly associated with psychological and physical health (495)
    A.   major life events
    B.   daily hassels
    C.   feelings of control
    D.   social support

277

23. People who believe they have control over their lives, health, and well-being are _____ than those who do not (508)
   A.   smarter
   B.   happier
   C.   harder workers
   D.   more successful in love and work

24. Amy was the first one to comfort Tom when the news broke about the death of his father. Amy could be said to provide Tom with (509)
   A.   networking
   B.   externalization
   C.   interreactance
   D.   social support

25. What do the physiological changes that accompany stress include? (501)
   A.   elevation of blood pressure
   B.   constriction of the pupils
   C.   increased production of gastric enzymes
   D.   all of the above

26. In which stage of the general adaptation syndrome is arousal level the highest? (491-492)
   A.   alarm
   B.   exhaustion
   C.   recovery
   D.   resistance

27. _____ refers to the stress experienced from living in the city. (498)
   A.   low socioeconomic status
   B.   PTSD
   C.   urban press
   D.   overload

28. Which term refers to the frequently occurring, repetitive sources of stress that happen to us on an almost daily basis? (495)
   A.   burnout
   B.   hassles
   C.   stressors
   D.   overload

29. Type B behavior is characterized by: (503)
   A.   anger
   B.   a sense of urgency
   C.   patience
   D.   competitiveness

30. Which group has a higher probability of suffering a heart attack? (504)
    A.   Anyone with Type A behavior pattern
    B.   Anyone with Type B behavior pattern
    C.   People who express their emotions vigorously
    D.   People who are hostile, angry and suspicious

31. According to Cohen's research, the _____ of stress are important in vulnerability
    to infection (506)
    A.   source and expression
    B.   site and cause
    C.   amount and duration
    D.   visualization and experience

32. The strategies and systems we have developed to let us deal more effectively with
    stressful situations are called (509)
    A.   social support
    B.   coping skills
    C.   general adaptation
    D.   health psychology

33. According to Aspinwall and Taylor, the first step in proactive coping is to (511)
    A.   recognize that a stressful situation is up coming
    B.   appraise the situation for potential difficulties
    C.   accumulate resources
    D.   devise a coping strategy

34. Environmental stimuli that may lead to physical or psychological injury to an organism
    is called (491)
    A..  frustrations
    B.   pressure
    C.   toxins
    D.   stressors

35. The most important component in determining whether an event is stressful is (491)
    A.   culture
    B.   appraisal
    C.   frequency
    D.   emotional stability

36. Stress inoculation refers to a set of strategies that are designed to help someone (512-
    513)
    A.   reduce their level of physiological reactance
    B.   identify the original cause of their stress reaction
    C.   measure the amount of stress they feel more accurately
    D.   cope effectively with an upcoming stressful situation

37. Health psychology is the subfield of psychology that focuses on (513)
    A. the appropriate psychological training for medical doctors
    B. the application of psychological principles to issues of health
    C. understanding unconscious motivations that make people ill
    D. developing better organizational structures for hospitals

38. In most parts of the world, AIDS is spread from person to person through (515)
    A. casual family contact
    B. contaminated food and water
    C. homosexual sex
    D. heterosexual sex

39. Severe stress caused by some type of disaster is called (497)
    A. psychogenic stress disorder
    B. delusional behavior
    C. catastrophic stress
    D. post traumatic stress

40. The belief that risky behaviors will be harmful to others but not to themselves is called (516)
    A. resilience
    B. optimistic bias
    C. stress inoculation
    D. external locus of control

41. In Selye's General Adaptation Syndrome, the focus is on _____ responses (491-492)
    A. physiological
    B. behavioral
    C. cognitive
    D. emotional

42. Research by Holmes and Rahe suggest that (493)
    A. only major events cause stress
    B. minor events cause more stress
    C. perception of stress causes stress
    D. combinations of life events cause stress

43. Stress management is the process individuals take to deal with varying situations. Psychologists call this process (507)
    A. time management
    B. resilience
    C. defense mechanisms
    D. coping

44. People who make changes in their normal routines and take specific actions designed to relieve illness and make them et well are said to be (517-518)
    A. psychopathological
    B. medically disturbed
    C. adopting a sick role
    D. hypochondriacal

45. Some people learn to keep their eyes open and focus on watching what is going on during a painful procedure, such as dental work, rather than closing their eyes and focusing on the pain. This is an example of a _____ approach to pain management (520)
    A. traditional
    B. behavior modification
    C. hypnotic
    D. chronic

# After You Have Finished

## Essay Questions:

1. Describe PTSD include its causes symptoms and effects as well as who is at risk. (497)

2. Describe two active coping styles and the effectiveness of each in different situations. (510-511)

3. What are some ways that health psychologists help individuals and communities lead healthier lives. (514-515)

4. How do feelings of control impact health? (508)

Describe the key components to Lazarus's view of stress. (493-495)

# Chapter 15

# Psychological Disorders

## Before you read...

Abnormal behavior today is characterized as atypical, socially unacceptable, distressing, maladaptive, and the result of distorted cognitions. As treatments have changed and different behaviors have become acceptable, this definition has changed. Before treatment plans are implemented, mental health professionals want to know something about the maladaptive behavior. To do this, they have used several models to outline the reasons for the maladjustment and to define treatment plans. The medical-biological model assumes a physical or biological basis for the disorder and therefore focuses on medical interventions. The psychodynamic model suggests that unresolved conflict and anxiety are at the root of the problem, and treatment focuses on resolving the conflicts. The humanistic model assumes that inner psychic forces are at work and focuses on the individual's uniqueness and decision making processes for treatment. The behavioral model asserts that faulty learning or conditioning lead to abnormal behavior and therefore that these behaviors can be unlearned or replaced. The cognitive model maintains that false assumptions and unrealistic coping strategies lead to abnormal behavior, and intervention focuses on changing these thought patterns. The sociocultural model contends that abnormal behavior occurs in the context of the family, community, or society.

The Diagnostic and Statistical Manual of Mental Disorders, Fourth Edition, is the most recent diagnostic manual. It consists of 16 major categories of maladjustment and more than 200 subcategories. The DSM-IV uses a multiaxial system for precise diagnosis. The goal of the DSM-IV and previous editions is to provide reliable diagnosis and assure that diagnosis is consistent with the research.

Anxiety disorders are discussed first. Generalized anxiety disorders are marked by chronic and persistent levels of anxiety in one of three areas of functioning: motor, autonomic, or vigilance. In phobic disorders irrational fears lead to avoidance behaviors that interfere with normal functioning. Obsessive-compulsive disorders (OCD) involve ritualistic behaviors to decrease anxiety.

Mood disorders which include bipolar disorders and depressive disorders may develop slowly or may be initiated by some traumatic event. Bipolar (manic-depressive) disorder is illustrated by extreme swings from mania to depression. Depressive disorders, including major depressive disorder, do not represent the vacillation between mania and depression. Major depression disorder is thought to be caused by a combination of biological, learning, and cognitive factors. Treatment should incorporate components of each model. When people suffer from major depression, they are at risk for suicide. A distinction is made between the attempters and the completers, as there are strong gender differences. The causes of suicide are not fully understood, but there is no dearth of attempts to explain why someone would resort to a fatal problem-solving technique.

Schizophrenia is one of the most perplexing, frustrating, and devastating mental disorders. Schizophrenics show significant deficits in cognitive functioning, perception, mood, and overall behavior. They can become delusional, experience hallucinations, display inappropriate affect, become depressed, and appear withdrawn or excited. There appears to be a strong biological basis for schizophrenia, and most treatments include pharmaceutical intervention. Some environmental factors have been suggested, but the focus remains on genetic predisposition being the major contributor, according to studies of high-risk children.

Personality disorders are usually long-standing maladaptive behaviors that begin in childhood or adolescence and continue through adulthood. These disorders are divided into three broad categories: odd or eccentric; fearful or anxious; or dramatic, emotional, and erratic. *Psychology* examines five specific personality disorders: the paranoid personality, the dependent personality, the histrionic personality, the narcissistic personality, and the antisocial personality disorders. The antisocial personality receives a lot of notoriety when criminals are diagnosed as being antisocial. Although child abuse is not classified as a personality disorder, many abusers suffer from other forms of personality disorder. *Psychology* also describes the violent act of rape as the behavior of a maladjusted person.

# Chapter Objectives

- List and describe five distinguishing characteristics of abnormal behavior and explain why psychologists prefer the term *maladjustment* to *abnormality*.
- Distinguish among the medical, psychodynamic, humanistic, behavioral, cognitive, sociocultural, and evolutionary models of abnormal behavior.
- Outline the goals of *DSM-IV*, list the five axes of the multiaxial system, and tell what each axis is intended to describe; also discuss some of psychologists' criticism and resistance to fully implementing the *DSM-IV*.
- Contrast the differing views of anxiety of Horney and Freud.
- Describe generalized anxiety disorder and list the three areas of impaired functioning.
- Define *phobic disorder* and characterize the differences between agoraphobia, social phobia, and specific phobia.
- Describe obsessive-compulsive disorder and name some typical ritualistic behaviors performed by persons with this disorder.
- Describe the symptoms of major depressive disorder, and list three methods used by clinicians to evaluate major depression.
- Summarize the causes of depression according to the biological, learning, cognitive, learned helplessness, and biopsychosocial theories.
- Identify the two phases of bipolar disorder, its prevalence in men and women, the typical age of onset, and success rate of treatment.
- Describe the symptoms normally seen in schizophrenic patients and characterize the different types of schizophrenia.
- Describe the hereditary and environmental factors that contribute to schizophrenia and identify its most likely causes.
- List and describe six personality disorders and discuss the biological components of antisocial personality disorder.
- Explain what is meant by the phrase *child abuse* and cite statistics concerning the rate of child abuse in the United States.
- Distinguish between suicide attempters and completers, cite some of the factors that may influence a suicide attempt, and list four steps you can take to help a person who is suicidal.

# As you read...

## What is Abnormal Behavior?

| 15-1 | A Definition |
|------|-------------|

1.    List the 5 characteristics of abnormal behavior.

2.    Define maladaptive.

3.    What is maladjustment?

4.    Describe the phenomenon of self-fulfilling prophecy.

5    Behavior characterized as: atypical, socially unacceptable, distressing, maladaptive and/or the result of distorted cognitions is called _____  _____.

| 15-2 | Perspectives on Abnormality |
|------|----------------------------|

6.    What is a model?

7.    Define abnormal psychology

8.    What is trephination?

9.    Describe the medical-biological model of abnormal behavior.

10.    What are some of the criticisms of the medical-biological model.

11.    Describe the psychodynamic model.

12.    In the _____ _____ of abnormal behavior, maladjustment occurs when a person's needs are not being met.

13. Describe the behavioral model.

14. A practitioner that believes maladaptive behaviors are the results of the client's thoughts subscribes to the _____ _____ of abnormal behavior.

15. What is the Sociocultural model of abnormal behavior?

16. Describe the evolutionary model.

| 15-3 | Diagnosing Psychopathology: The DSM |
|------|-------------------------------------|

17. What is the DSM?

18. Define prevalence.

19. Describe the 5 axes of the DSM.

20. What are some of the criticisms of the DSM?

21. Describe the case study of C.

22. How does culture impact diagnosis and treatment?

# Anxiety Disorders

| 15-4 | Defining Anxiety |
|------|------------------|

1. Define anxiety.

2. How does Horney view anxiety and maladjustment?

3. How did Freud view anxiety?

4.    What is neurosis?


5.    Define free-floating anxiety.


6.    Anxiety is a _____ of maladjustment but not necessarily the
_____ of maladjustment.


## 15-5    Generalized Anxiety Disorder

7.    Describe generalized anxiety disorder.


8.    What types of symptoms do people with generalized anxiety disorder experience?


9.    According to the DSM, a person with generalized anxiety disorder must have
persistent anxiety that is _____ _____ to any one situation.


## 15-6    Phobic Disorders

10.    Define phobic disorder.


11.    How are phobias maintained?


12.    In order for something to be considered a phobia, both _____ and
_____ must be apparent.


13.    Define agoraphobia.


14.    What are panic attacks?


15.    The fear of being alone in a large public place without being able to escape is
_____.

16.    A _____ _____ is an anxiety disorder which is characterized by a fear of being embarrassed or scrutinized in a humiliating way.

17.    Define specific phobia.

18.    List some of the specific phobias.

---

## 15-7    Obsessive-Compulsive Disorder

19.    Define obsessive-compulsive disorder.

20.    A person with obsessive-compulsive disorder reduces tension by performing _____ _____.

21.    Describe how the psychodynamic theorists, behaviorists and biopsychologists explain obsessive-compulsive disorder.

# Mood Disorders

## 15-8    Depressive Disorders

1.    Define depressive disorders.

2.    What is major depressive disorder?

3.    List some of the symptoms of major depressive disorder.

4.    Depressed people often have false beliefs or _____.

5.    What is reality testing?

6.    What is rumination?

7. Describe the 3 parts of a clinical evaluation.

8. What is dysthymic disorder?

## 15-9 Causes of Major Depressive Disorder

9. Describe the biological theory of major depressive disorders.

10. List the 4 monoamines.

11. _____ is when a neuron takes back up a neurotransmitter it has released.

12. What is the monoamine theory of depression?

13. Describe Leinsohn's view of depression.

14. What is Beck's view of depression?

15. The behavior of giving up or not responding is called _____
_____.

16. Define vulnerability.

17. Describe the diathesis-stress model.

## 15-10 Bipolar Disorder

18. Define bipolar disorder.

19. Describe the 2 phases of bipolar disorder.

20.    List some of the symptoms of bipolar disorder.

# Dissociative Disorders

| 15-11  Dissociative Amnesia |
| --- |

1.    Define dissociative disorders.

2.    What is dissociative amnesia?

3.    What is a common cause of dissociative amnesia?

| 15-12  Dissociative Indentity: Multiple Personality |
| --- |

4.    Define dissociative identity disorder.

5.    Switching from one personality to another is often brought on by _____.

6.    What arguments are given for and against dissociative disorder?

# Schizophrenia

1.    Describe schizophrenic disorders.

2.    Define psychotic.

| 15-13  Essential Characteristics of Schizophrenic Disorders |
| --- |

3.    What are the positive and negative symptoms of schizophrenia?

4.    What are delusions of grandeur?

5.     How is memory impacted by schizophrenia?


6.     Perceptual experiences that occur without any physical stimulus are called
_____.


7.     Describe inappropriate affect.


8.     What is ambivalent affect?


## 15-14   Types of Schizophrenia

9.     Describe the 5 types of schizophrenia.


10.    People with the _____ type of schizophrenia have a relatively low level of
cognitive impairment.


11.    Distinguish between the excited catatonic and withdrawn catatonic types of
schizophrenia.

12.    People who exhibit all the features of schizophrenia, but do not fit into the other 4
categories have _____ type of schizophrenia.


13.    Match the following subcategories of Schizophrenic Disorder with the appropriate
description.
          *Disorganized Type, Paranoid Type, Catatonic Type, Residual Type,*
                    *Undifferentiated Type*

   A) _____ _____: Characterized by stupor in which individuals
      are mute, negative, and basically unresponsive.  Characteristics can also
      include displays of excited or violent motor activity.  Individuals can
      switch from the *withdrawn* to the *excited* state.
   B) _____ _____: Characterized by frequent incoherence, absence
      of systematized delusions, and blunted, inappropriate, or silly affect.
   C) _____ _____: Characterized by prominent delusions,
      hallucinations, incoherence, or grossly disorganized behavior and does not
      meet the criteria for any other type or meets the criteria for more than one
      other type.

D) _____ _____: Characterized by delusions and hallucinations of persecution and/or grandeur; irrational jealousy is sometimes evident.

E) _____ _____: Characterized by a history of at least one previous episode of schizophrenia with prominent psychotic symptoms, a current state of being in touch with reality, and signs of inappropriate affect, illogical thinking, social withdrawal, or eccentric behavior.

---

**15-15  Causes of Schizophrenia**

14.    How does the diathesis-stress model apply to schizophrenia?

15.    Describe the evidence that exists for biological factors of schizophrenia.

16.    Define concordance rate.

17.    What is the dopamine theory of schizophrenia?

18.    What areas of the brain are involved in obsessive-compulsive disorder?

19.    What areas of the brain are involved in depression?

20.    What structural differences have been seen in the brains of schizophrenics?

21.    What environmental factors influence schizophrenia?

22.    What is a double bind?

# Personality Disorders

1.    Define personality disorders.

2.    Describe the 3 broad classes of personality disorders.

3.    List and describe the 6 personality disorders given in the chapter.


4.    The personality disorder characterized by instability of interpersonal relationships, self-image and affect is _____.


5.    Research has shown that people with _____ personality disorder do not have normal autonomic nervous system reactions to fear.


# Violence and Mental Disorders

## 15-16  Diagnoses Associated with Violence

1.    How is schizophrenia associated with violence?


2.    Describe the types of damage that can be done by people with antisocial personality disorder.


3.    What is the legal definition of insanity?


4.    People with mental disorders are more likely to commit _____ than violence against another person.


5.    Distinguish between attempters and completers.


6.    What are the warning signs of suicide?


7.    What steps would you take if someone you know is suicidal?


## 15-17  Violence as a Risk for Developing Mental Disorders

8.    Define child abuse.

9. Define intimate partner violence.
10. A forced sexual assault on an unconsenting partner is called
    _____.


11. What is date rape?

**Term Identification: Make flashcards for each of the following terms. Hint: Use the definitions in the margins of the chapter**

Abnormal Behavior
Model
Abnormal Psychology
Prevalence
Case Study
Anxiety
Generalized Anxiety Disorder
Phobic Disorders
Agoraphobia
Panic Attacks
Social Phobia
Specific Phobia
Obsessive-Compulsive Disorder
Depressive Disorders
Major Depressive Disorder
Delusions
Learned Helplessness
Vulnerability

Bipolar Disorder
Dissociative Disorders
Dissociative Amnesia
Dissociative Identity Disorder
Schizophrenic Disorders
Psychotic
Disorganized Type of Schizophrenia
Paranoid Type of Schizophrenia
Catatonic Type of Schizophrenia
Residual Type of Schizophrenia
Undifferentiated Type of Schizophrenia
Concordance Rate
Double Bind
Personality Disorders
Antisocial Personality Disorder
Child Abuse
Rape

# After you read . . . Self Test

## Chapter 15 Self Test

1.  The use of the term maladjustment rather than abnormal to describe behavior is important because: (527)
    A.  it implies that the behavior is treatable.
    B.  it does not carry social stigma.
    C.  it is less vague and makes diagnosis easier.
    D.  none of the above

2.  Practitioners who treat maladjusted behavior by teaching people how to develop new thought processes that instill new values is an example of the_____ model of abnormal behavior. (529)
    A.  behavioral
    B.  biological
    C.  humanistic
    D.  cognitive

3.  Some psychologists, such as Thomas Szasz, dislike our entire system of characterizing mental illness, claiming that (527)
    A.  all cases of mental illness are actually due to an underlying physical cause
    B.  labeling people in this way only makes them appear more abnormal
    C.  it is the psychoanalysts' own disorder that makes them see illness in others
    D.  modern society is causing mental disorder, and society must be changed

4.  Which field of psychology focuses on the assessment, treatment, and prevention of maladaptive behaviors? (528)
    A.  health psychology
    B.  personality psychology
    C.  community psychology
    D.  abnormal psychology

5.  A Specific phobia is: (537)
    A.  any phobia of a specific object or situation, along with a compelling desire to avoid it.
    B.  the normal everyday hesitations that we all experience.
    C.  easy to diagnose but very difficult to modify.
    D.  a fear of having to put forth effort or commitment.

6. Which of the following illustrates an obsessive-compulsive disorder? (538)
   A. Mary's desk is always neat because she spends fifteen minutes each day before leaving work putting things in order.
   B. Sam makes a point of checking to see that he has unplugged the coffee pot before going to work because he worries about small appliances causing fires.
   C. Mark loves sports and watches every television sports show he can.
   D. Elida mops the kitchen floor three times before preparing a meal because she fears it is infested with mites, and she cannot feel comfortable exposing food until she has finished her mopping.

7. Lynda's therapist believes that her compulsive behavior is caused by a chemical abnormality in her brain, and has prescribed medication to treat it. This therapist probably subscribes to the _____ model of abnormality (528)
   A. medical-biological
   B. cognitive
   C. psychodynamic
   D. eclectic

8. Which model views behavior by focusing on the uniqueness and decision making? (529)
   A. the social model
   B. the cognitive model
   C. the behavioral model
   D. the humanistic model

9. The words "smooth operator" and "superficial charm" would be used to describe: (557)
   A. an exhibitionist.
   B. antisocial personality.
   C. histrionic personality.
   D. narcissistic personality.

10. People diagnosed as having antisocial personalities: (557)
    A. constantly blame themselves for their own problems.
    B. do not fear or learn from punishment.
    C. conform only so that they may avoid feelings of shame and guilt.
    D. have insight into how their behavior affects others.

11. The psychodynamic model of abnormality is based primarily on the psychological theories of (529)
    A. B.F. Skinner
    B. Abraham Maslow
    C. Sigmund Freud
    D. Wilhelm Wundt

12. Alan's therapist believes that his immaturity and temper tantrums are due to his parents consistently giving him what he wanted whenever he threw a tantrum. This therapist probably agrees with the _____ model of abnormality. (529)
    A.  psychodynamic
    B.  cognitive
    C.  legal
    D.  behavioral

13. Which perspective on abnormality focuses on the importance of one's family and community on the development and expression of maladaptive behaviors? (529)
    A.  psychoanalytic model
    B.  legal model
    C.  the behavioral model
    D.  the sociocultural model

14. If a psychologist says that a depressed patient is showing delusions, we can assume that the psychologist means the patient: (541)
    A.  is displaying false beliefs.
    B.  will talk excessively.
    C.  is evaluating the consequences of suicide.
    D.  has had a recurrence of a depressive episode.

15. People who exhibit symptoms of major depressive disorder: (541)
    A.  are usually unable to explain why their response is prolonged.
    B.  may need to be hospitalized.
    C.  usually blame their loved ones for their problems.
    D.  are too depressed to consider suicide.

16. When working with the DSM-IV, a psychologist will use the third axes to describe the individual's (532)
    A.  major psychological disorder
    B.  overall level of functioning
    C.  current physical condition
    D.  social and environmental situation

17. Which of the following is *not* an explanation offered by learning theorists about the cause of major depressions?  Depressed people: (544-545)
    A.  lack prosocial behaviors and are avoided or punished because of the behaviors they do emit.
    B.  have negative views and expectations about the human condition.
    C.  experience an imbalance in certain body chemicals when they are involved in stress inducing situations.
    D.  feel they have no control over the consequences of their behavior.

18. Schizophrenia affects _____ individuals. (549)
    A.   1 out of 10
    B.   1 out of 100
    C.   1 out of 1,000
    D.   1 out of 10,000

19. A delusion is: (541)
    A.   a false belief that is inconsistent with reality.
    B.   a perceptual malfunction that causes a person to hear voices of people who are not present.
    C.   an incoherent and random pattern of thinking.
    D.   all of the above

20. _____ Type schizophrenics are among the most difficult to identify because their outward behavior frequently seems appropriate to their situation. (551)
    A.   Disorganized
    B.   Paranoid
    C.   Catatonic
    D.   Undifferentiated

21. A prominent characteristic in catatonic type schizophrenia is: (551)
    A.   the presence of delusions of persecution and grandeur.
    B.   extreme overt behavior that involves either excessive motor and verbal activity or a severe decline in motor and verbal activity.
    C.   the lack of good personal hygiene.
    D.   the absence of systematized delusions.

22. People who show symptoms attributable to a schizophrenic disorder but who remain in touch with reality are diagnosed as _____ type. (552-553)
    A.   Disorganized
    B.   Undifferentiated
    C.   Residual
    D.   B and C

23. Those psychologists who explain the development of schizophrenic disorders as a combination of nature and nurture would suggest that: (556)
    A.   if one twin has schizophrenia, the other twin also will develop the disorder.
    B.   contentious parents who minimize closeness and warmth will produce schizophrenic offspring.
    C.   brain impairment left undiagnosed will produce schizophrenia.
    D.   a genetic predisposition triggered by environmental stressors may lead to a behavioral pattern of schizophrenia.

24. Research on the relationship between ethnicity and the diagnosis of psychological disorder has found that (533)
    A.   genetic factors cause most differences in ethnic groups
    B.   minorities are systematically denied mental health services
    C.   certain diagnoses are more common in some ethnic groups
    D.   minorities consistently receive more severe diagnoses

25. A vague, general uneasiness or an ominous feeling that something bad is about to happen is called (535)
   A.   neurosis
   B.   guilt
   C.   conscience
   D.   anxiety

26. Rachel feels an almost constant sense of fear and worry, as thought something terrible were about to happen, but she can't figure out anything specific that worries her. Rachel is most likely to suffer from (536)
   A.   obsessive-compulsive disorder
   B.   hypochondriasis
   C.   dissociative amnesia
   D.   generalized anxiety disorder

27. Select the criterion used by the law to define "insane." (559)
   A.   statistical frequency
   B.   intellectually competent
   C.   responsibility for behavior
   D.   social acceptability

28. What is the acronym for the most widely accepted system for identifying psychological disorders? (533)
   A.   MMPI
   B.   K-ABC
   C.   EVE
   D.   DSM-IV

29. What is the primary goal of the DSM-IV? (531)
   A.   organize disorders into categories on the basis of etiological evidence
   B.   improve the reliability of diagnosis
   C.   introduce a common terminology into the mental health field
   D.   describe preventative measures

30. When is anxiety described as "free-floating?" (535)
   A.   It comes and goes for no apparent reason.
   B.   It accompanies agoraphobia.
   C.   There is not obvious source or cause.
   D.   It is not accompanied by autonomic nervous system arousal

31. Agoraphobia involves the strong fear and avoidance of (537)
   A.   being alone in a public places that are hard to get out of
   B.   any specific object or situation that is not really dangerous
   C.   interacting with or being observed by other individuals
   D.   any small, confined space with no obvious way out

32. Which of the following disorders can produce crooked politicians, unscrupulous business persons, deceptive salespeople, and violent criminals? (557)
   A.   paranoid
   B.   antisocial
   C.   avoidant
   D.   histrionic

33. What is the most frequently occurring psychological disorder? (541-542)
   A.   depression
   B.   schizophrenia
   C.   bipolar disorder
   D.   phobias

34. In which type of schizophrenia are symptoms the most severe and bizarre? (552)
   A.   undifferentiated
   B.   paranoid
   C.   disorganized
   D.   catatonic

35. Which of the following is not a criterion for defining abnormal behavior (526)
   A.   maladaptive
   B.   socially unacceptable
   C.   disturbing to others
   D.   distorted cognitions

36. Which model of abnormality emphasizes hospitalization and drug treatment programs (528)
   A.   Humanistic
   B.   Medical-biological
   C.   Psychodynamic
   D.   Sociocultural

37. An important feature of the DSM-IV is (531)
   A.   prevalence rates
   B.   specific treatment plans
   C.   drug intervention options
   D.   probability of cure

38. Karen has a persistent feeling of anxiety and an impending sense of doom but, her anxiety is not related to any specific object or situation. She is suffering from (535)
   A.   agoraphobia
   B.   free floating anxiety
   C.   social phobia
   D.   obsessive-compulsive disorder

39. John's roommate keeps his room immaculate and washes his hands all the time. He claims he is just trying to avoid getting germs and becoming contaminated. He may be suffering from (538)
    A. somatoform disorder
    B. germaphobia
    C. psyhogenic trauma
    D. obsessive compulsive disorder

40. A disorder that involves unwarranted fear and feelings of persecution and mistrust is (557)
    A. histrionic personality disorder
    B. paranoid personality disorder
    C. inadequate personality disorder
    D. dependent personality disorder

41. Missy is constantly complaining about her boyfriend and telling wild stories about how he treats her. She also flirts with other boys and asks about how they would treat her if they were dating. She might be diagnosed with (557)
    A. borderline personality disorder
    B. narcissistic personality disorder
    C. conversion disorder
    D. histrionic personality disorder

42. Beth is one of the most active parents in Meghan's school. She is involved in almost school project and like to be in charge. Occasionally, she will be absent for several days at a time and forget about her responsibilities. She could be diagnosed with (546)
    A. bipolar disorder
    B. dependent personality disorder
    C. narcissistic personality disorder
    D. major depression

43. According to the learning and cognitive theories of depression, (544-545)
    A. people are born with a predisposition to become depressed
    B. people who fail become addicted to failure
    C. people learn from their environment
    D. people have chemical imbalances leading to depression

44. Suicide is most highly correlated with (560)
    A. personality disorders
    B. somataform disorders
    C. dissociative disorders
    D. depressive disorders

45. Andy claims that he knows about the governments plan to influence people's minds via the internet. He fears that if he tells anyone the government will have him assassinated. Andy may be diagnosed as having (551)
    A. paranoid schizophrenia
    B. delusions of grandeur
    C. disorganized schizophrenia
    D. rational thoughts

# When You Have Finished

## Essay Questions:

1.      What is maladjusted behavior and its 5 characteristics? (526-527)

2.      How is a phobia different from a fear and how are phobias treated? (536-538)

3.      Describe the diathesis-stress model and its role in depression and schizophrenia. (545-546, 553-554)

4.      How do the different models of abnormality account for obsessive-compulsive disorder? (539)

5.      Describe the biological theory of depression and its criticisms. (543-544)

# Chapter 16

# Therapy

## Before you read...

There are two broad categories of therapy: biologically based therapies and psychotherapy. Biologically based therapies, sometimes called somatic therapies, treat psychological disorders with medical and pharmaceutical strategies. Psychotherapies, on the other hand, treat psychological disorders through psychological techniques. There is no *magic bullet;* treatment of psychological disorders requires proper diagnosis, an understanding of the contributing factors, and the right treatment strategy. Research on the effectiveness of psychotherapy concludes that it is effective with a wide variety of disorders. Is one therapy more effective that another? There are more than 200 types of psychotherapeutic approaches, some focus on individuals, some on families, and some on communities. In determining the effectiveness of a therapeutic approach, one must also consider the dynamics of the individual, the therapist, and the culture from which the client comes. In general, the therapist and client must work together for treatment to be effective.

Psychoanalysis (Freudian therapy) is an insight therapy and attempts to discover relationships between unconscious motives and behavior. Psychoanalysis use techniques such as free association, dream analysis, and interpretation. Additionally, resistance and transference are seen as central processes essential for effective treatment. Some of Freud's followers differ in their beliefs concerning the contributions of the ego. These ego-analysts assume people have voluntary control over their urges and therefore can be helped if they learn to master their egos. Criticisms of psychodynamically based therapies are discussed.

Uniqueness and free will are the focus of humanistic therapies. Roger's client-centered approach is nondirective. The client determines the direction of therapy while the therapist remains somewhat passive. The therapist must be warm and accepting of the client and show unconditional positive regard. Gestalt therapy examines the here-and-now of the client and tries to put him or her in touch with feelings. Hypnosis is used as an adjunct to many therapeutic approaches.

Behavior therapy (behavior modification) sees maladaptive behavior as learned behavior. Behaviorists assume that people are not abnormal, but are having trouble with a life situation, and they can learn to cope with the situation, and the maladaptive behavior will cease. Operant conditioning, counterconditioning, and modeling are three major behavioral techniques. Operant conditioning is useful with a wide variety of behaviors in a variety of settings. Counterconditioning teaches new, more adaptive responses to familiar stimuli. Modeling is effective with new behaviors, fear reduction, and enhancing existing behaviors.

Cognitive therapists offer three basic propositions: (1) thought affects behavior, (2) thoughts can be monitored, and (3) behavior will change through thought change. Rational emotive therapy (RET) emphasizes the role of logical, rational thoughts. Maladaptive behavior is the result of irrational beliefs and faulty thinking. Beck also supports the role of irrational thoughts, and the goal is to develop more positive, realistic perceptions of the self and the world. Meichenbaum believes that people are what they say to themselves and restating (self-instruction) the event will result in more adaptive behaviors. Brief intermittent therapy is discussed as a newer cognitive approach.

Group therapy may follow any approach and involves putting together a group of people, usually with similar problems, to support each other in resolving their problems. Family therapy involves changing family systems by changing some of the family interactions. *Psychology* reviews the family problem of codependence.
Biologically based therapies may be used in conjunction with other psychological treatment approaches. These approaches may involve medication, hospitalization, and the involvement of physicians. Psychosurgery, electroconvulsive shock, and drug therapy are examples of biologically based psychotherapy. Recent research with depression indicates that psychotherapy is especially effective for treating depression, and that drug therapy is not necessary.

# Chapter Objectives

- Briefly distinguish between biologically based therapy and psychotherapy and Summarize and discuss the research findings concerning the overall effectiveness of psychotherapy.

- Identify the different orientations to psychotherapy and describe the steps one would go through in choosing a therapy and a therapist.

- Distinguish between psychoanalysis and psychodynamically based therapy, and state the basic assumptions and the goal of insight therapies. Describe the various techniques used in psychoanalysis and discuss the psychoanalytic concepts of resistance, transference, and interpretation as a process.

- Explain how ego analysis differs from psychoanalysis and discuss some of the criticisms and problems surrounding psychoanalysis.

- Outline the goals, techniques, and assumptions of client-centered therapy and discuss some common criticisms of this approach.

- Differentiate among psychodynamic, humanistic, and behavior therapies by describing the reasons why behaviorists are dissatisfied with psychodynamic and humanistic therapies; also, discuss the debate surrounding symptom substitution.

- List the three general procedures involved in behavior therapy and describe the techniques and principles used in operant conditioning to establish desired behaviors and decrease undesired behaviors.

- Describe the goals of counterconditioning and explain how behavior therapists apply the principle of classical conditioning when they use systematic desensitization and aversive counterconditioning.

- Describe three effective uses of modeling according to Bandura and discuss the problems that may occur when people imitate the behavior of inappropriate models.

- State the three basic assumptions of cognitive therapy and the focus of cognitive restructuring. State the basic assumption and major goal of rational-emotive therapy.

- Describe the causes of maladaptive behavior according to Beck and list the four stages a successful client passes through. Then briefly describe Meichenbaum's self instructional therapeutic technique.

- Describe the assumptions and focus of family therapy and discuss some of the difficulties involved in the effort to change family systems.

- Describe four classes of psychotropic drugs, give examples of each, and state types of disorders for which they might be prescribed.

- Explain why psychologists might sometimes resort to biologically based therapies such as psychosurgery and electroconvulsive shock.

# As you read...

## Therapy Comes in Many Forms

1.  Define somatic therapy.


2.  What is psychotherapy?


---

**16-1    Is Psychotherapy Necessary and Effective**

3.  Define placebo effect.


4.  What is the double-blind technique?


5.  What are demand characteristics?


6.  List some signs of good progress in therapy.


---

**16-2    Which Therapy, Which Therapist?**

7.  What are community psychologists?


8.  Describe the psychodynamically based approaches to therapy.


9.  Define humanistic therapy.


10.  What is behavior therapy?


11.  Therapy that focuses on changing behaviors by changing thoughts is called
    _____ _____.


12.  Describe psychotherapy integration.

13. What 2 things does prevention research focus on?

14. What conclusions can be drawn from the smoking prevention study?

| 16-3 | Culture and Gender Therapy |
| --- | --- |

15. What is multiculturalism?

16. Define transculturalism.

17. How does culture affect therapy?

18. What gender differences exist in therapy?

| 16-4 | Managed Care and Psychology |
| --- | --- |

19. What are the 3 key components to managed care?

20. What are the 2 problems with managed care?

21. Describe brief therapy.

22. What question does an operational diagnosis answer?

23. What questions should you ask in choosing a therapist?

# Psychoanalysis and Psychodynamic Therapies

24. Define psychoanalysis.

25. What are psychodynamically based therapies?

26.    What are the 2 basic assumptions of insight therapy?

27.    Insight therapy has a goal of treating the _____ of abnormal behaviors.

| 16-5    Goals of Psychoanalysis |

28.    What is the general goal of psychoanalysis?

29.    What are 3 goals of psychoanalysis?

| 16-6    Techniques of Psychoanalysis |

30.    Describe free association.

31.    What is dream analysis?

32.    What are defense mechanisms?

34.    Match the following therapeutic techniques and patient responses with the
        appropriate description:
        *free association, dream analysis, interpretation, resistance, transference*

        A) _____ The therapist becomes the object of the patients
        emotional attitudes about a person in the patient's life.
        B) _____ Patients are asked to describe in detail, used to gain
        insight into unconscious motivations.
        C) _____ A common occurrence in psychoanalysis, where the
        patient shows through some kind of behavior an unwillingness to cooperate
        with the therapist.
        D) _____ A major part of free association and dream analysis.
        The analyst tries to discern common threads in the patient's behavior and
        thoughts.
        E) _____ Patient is asked to report whatever comes to mind.
        The purpose is to recognize connections and allow the unconscious to express
        itself uncensored.

34.    Describe working through.

35.    Who are ego analysts?

36.    Distinguish between traditional psychoanalysts and ego analysts.

37.    What are the criticisms of psychoanalysis?

# Humanistic Therapies

1.    Describe client-centered therapy.

2.    What 3 things must a person have in a relationship to reach their full potential?

3.    What are the basic assumptions of Roger's approach to therapy?

4.    How is client-centered therapy different from psychoanalysis?

5.    When a therapist projects positive feelings toward a client it is called _____ _____ _____.

6.    What is empathic listening?

7.    Describe the client after successful therapy.

8.    What are the criticisms of client-centered therapy?

# Behavior Therapy

| 16-8 | Goals of Behavior Therapy |

1.    Describe behavior modifications.

2.     How is behavior therapy different from the insight therapies?

3.     What are the 3 reasons behaviorists are dissatisfied with psychodynamic and humanistic therapies?

4.     What is symptom substitution?

---

**16-9     Techniques of Behavior Therapy**

5.     What are the 3 general procedures of behavior therapy?

6.     When is behavior therapy considered to have been effective?

---

**16-10   Operant Conditioning**

7.     What is a reinforcer?

8.     How does operant conditioning work as therapy?

9.     Define token economy.

10.    Describe the token economy set up by Lefton.

11.    Define extinction.

12.    Define punishment.

13.    What problems are there with punishment?

14.    What is a time-out?

15.     Define counterconditioning?

16.     What are the 3 stages of systematic desensitization?

17.     Describe aversive counterconditioning.


**16-12  Modeling**

18.     Define modeling.

19.     When is modeling most effective as a behavior therapy technique?

20.     Can problem drinkers become social drinkers?


# Cognitive Therapies

1.      Describe cognitive therapy.

2.      What are the 3 basic propositions of cognitive therapy?

3.      Define cognitive restructuring.


**16-13  Three Therapies**

4.      What is rational emotive therapy?

5.      What is the major goal of rational emotive therapy?

6.      Describe Beck's approach to cognitive therapy.

7.   List the 4 stages of Beck's therapy.

8.   Describe Meichenbaum's approach.

# Group Therapies

### 16-14  Techniques and Formats

9.   Define group therapy.

10.   What is the format of group therapy?

11.   Although the duration of group therapy varies, over _____ _____ is usual.

### 16-15  Family Therapy

12.   What is family therapy?

13.   How is family defined?

14.   What is relationship therapy?

15.   How is family an interactive system?

16.   _____ is when the entire family becomes enmeshed in one family members problem.

17.   What characteristics might a codependents have?

# Biologically Based Therapies

## 16-16   Drug Therapy

1.      What are psychotropic drugs?


2.      Describe antianxiety drugs and list some of them.


3.      What are antidepressants?


4.      How do the SSRIs work?


5.      Why is Prozac so popular?


6.      What problems are there with Prozac?


7.      How do the tricyclics work?


8.      Drugs that break down the enzyme, monoamine oxidase, are called _____
        _____ _____.


9.      Describe antimania drugs.


10.     What do antipsychotic drugs accomplish?


11.     Describe tardive dyskinesia.


## 16-17   Psychosurgery and Electroconclusive Therapy

12.     Define psychosurgery.


13.     What is a frontal lobotomy?

14. _____ _____ is a treatment for severe mental illness in which a shock of electricity is applied to the head.

15.    When is ECT most effective?

Psychotherapy
Placebo Effect
Double-Blind Technique
Demand Characteristics
Psychoanalysis
Psychodynamically Based
Therapies
Insight Therapy
Free Association
Dream Analysis
Interpretation
Resistance
Transference
Working Through

Client-Centered Therapy
Behavior Therapy
Symptom Substitution
Token Economy
Time-out
Counterconditioning
Systematic Desensitization
Aversive Counterconditioning
Rational-Emotive Therapy
Group Therapy
Family Therapy
Psychosurgery
Electroconvulsive Therapy

# After you read . . . Self Test

## Chapter 16 Self Test:

1.  Psychotherapy typically refers to treatment that involves: (569)
    A.  the manipulation of diet and physical exercise.
    B.  the use of electroconvulsive shock and prescriptions for tranquilizers and antipsychotic drugs.
    C.  techniques based upon psychological principles.
    D.  all of the above

2.  A psychologist who works with groups and neighborhoods to develop an action-oriented approach to individual and social adjustment is a _____ psychologist. (571)
    A.  social
    B.  community
    C.  physiological.
    D.  clinical

3.  Clinical psychologists who use therapeutic techniques that are rooted in Freudian theories: (571)
    A.  usually have been specifically trained in psychoanalysis.
    B.  refer to their therapies as psychodynamic therapy.
    C.  focus on the treatment of actual behavior problems rather than on the causes of the behavior problem.
    D.  all of the above

4.  The purpose of techniques such as dream analysis and free association is to: (579)
    A.  encourage the patient to talk about events in the "here and now."
    B.  observe the frequency of thoughts that arise from the reality principle.
    C.  clarify the patient's point of view concerning his or her behavior.
    D.  gain access to thoughts in the unconscious.

5.  The therapist is empathic, understanding, very attentive and yet the patient continues to respond to him as if he is not going to hear, care about, or accept what she has to say. After many months of therapy, both the therapist and patient realize that as a child the patient was constantly exposed to the attitude "children should be seen and not heard." Her behavior toward the therapist illustrates: (580)
    A.  interpretation.
    B.  resistance.
    C.  transference.
    D.  reaction formation.

319

6. Ego-analysis assumes that: (580)
   A. because it is such a lengthy process, psychoanalysis is not the most appropriate method for treatment.
   B. uprooting unconscious material in the id and superego should be the focus of treatment.
   C. increasing the patient's ego control.
   D. therapy should focus on developing the part of the personality that responds realistically to the demands of the environment.

7. When looking at the effectiveness of psychotherapy, in general and psychoanalysis, in particular, research suggests that they are: (580-581)
   A. always more effective than no therapy at all.
   B. effective within a narrow range of situations.
   C. selectively effective; the effectiveness varies with the disorder being treated.
   D. ineffective.

8. The form of therapy devised by Freud is_____; modern therapies that are loosely based on his model are _____. (578)
   A. psychoanalysis; psychodynamically based therapies
   B. ego analysis; rational-emotive therapies
   C. internal analysis; counterconditioning therapies
   D. meta-analysis; psychotropic drug therapies

9. A psychotherapist who urges a client to express freely thoughts and feelings and to verbalize whatever comes to mind without editing or censoring is using the technique of: (579)
   A. transference
   B. interpretation
   C. free association
   D. abreaction

10. The primary technique used in client-centered therapy is: (582-583)
    A. counterconditioning.
    B. interpretation.
    C. direct suggestion.
    D. a concentrated, warm, and accepting work atmosphere.

11. What do psychoanalysts suspect is occurring when patients become angry, or miss appointments (579)
    A. resistance
    B. transference
    C. working through
    D. revelation

12. An important difference between humanistic and psychoanalytic therapies is that humanistic therapies emphasize (581)
    A.   the environmental reinforcers that control behaviors
    B.   the importance of achieving insight into one's problems
    C.   the control of behavior by hidden, unconscious conflicts
    D.   the uniqueness, creativity and free will of the clients

13. Behavior therapists are dissatisfied with insight therapies for all of the following reasons *except*: (585)
    A.   They find many of the terms used by insight therapists to be difficult to define and measure.
    B.   They disagree with insight therapist's belief that most maladjustments must be changed by the person with the behavior problem.
    C.   They feel that the labels used by insight therapists can themselves cause maladaptive behavior.
    D.   They question the effectiveness of insight therapies.

14. The type of therapy developed by Carl Rogers is (581)
    A.   Gestalt therapy
    B.   existential therapy
    C.   client-centered therapy
    D.   attributional therapy

15. A behavior therapist knows that treatment has been effective when: (586)
    A.   symptom substitution can be noticeably measured.
    B.   the client says he has learned new coping skills.
    C.   follow-up observations show that the new behavior is still occurring.
    D.   all of the above

16. In operant conditioning positive reinforcement is used in all of the following ways *except*: It is (37-42)
    A.   delivered contingent upon desired behaviors.
    B.   removed to decrease the frequency of undesired behaviors.
    C.   used in combination with extinction and punishment procedures.
    D.   used to purge hidden maladjustments prior to implementing a behavior modification treatment plan.

17. In a token economy the number of tokens a person receives is usually dependent on: (586-587)
    A.   a variable-interval schedule of reinforcement.
    B.   the time of day or the day of the week.
    C.   the number of privileges the person desires.
    D.   the level of difficulty of the behavior emitted.

18. If Robin's parents ignore her every time she makes irritating noises in hopes of getting their attention, behavior therapists would say they are: (587)
    A.   using a technique called extinction.
    B.   neglecting the child's cries for help.
    C.   punishing the child for a socially unacceptable behavior.
    D.   trying to control the child's behavior through counterconditioning.

19. When aversive counterconditioning is used, the patient: (590)
    A.   is forced into a high anxiety state until he or she sees that the problem behavior is unreasonable.
    B.   gradually becomes less emotional.
    C.   learns a new behavior in response to a stimulus that needs to be avoided.
    D.   learns to challenge fear-producing stimuli.

20. Behavior therapists would say a child's fear of dogs diminishes when she observes other children playing with dogs, because of _____ therapy. (590)
    A.   operant conditioning
    B.   modeling
    C.   cognitive restructuring
    D.   play

21. Rational-emotive therapy: (593-594)
    A.   tries to place a person's cognitive assumptions about their experiences in a reasonable framework.
    B.   encourages people to put a high value on the things they want to get out of life.
    C.   is based on the idea that abnormal behaviors cause irrational thoughts.
    D.   is best described as a self-help technique.

22. From a family therapist's point of view, the patient in family therapy is: (597)
    A.   the family member who is used as a scapegoat.
    B.   the family member or members who do the scapegoating.
    C.   the parents.
    D.   the family structure and organization.

23. A therapist who communicates to a client a warm, personal attitude that the client is good, worthwhile, loveable human being no matter what the client says or does is displaying (582-583)
    A.   free association
    B.   counterconditioning
    C.   unconditional positive regard
    D.   emotional transerence

24. One of the advantages of group therapy is: (597)
    A.   members model behavior for one another.
    B.   a member can talk about a behavior problem without having to face social pressure to change.
    C.   the therapist is more directive enabling therapy to proceed more quickly.
    D.   all of the above

25. The specific composition of a group involved in group therapy usually: (597)
    A.  occurs by chance.
    B.  is the result of one avid member who solicits others to join the group.
    C.  depends on legal and medical referrals.
    D.  is controlled by the therapist's selection of who can gain from and offer to the group's purpose.

26. An important criticism of client-centered therapies is that (583)
    A.  there is not enough emphasis on biological factors
    B.  warm feelings may not be enough to help people change
    C.  it focuses too much on behavior, not enough on feelings
    D.  it makes clients feel too distant and uncomfortable.

27. When a symptom has been eliminated through therapy, but another symptom appears to take its place it is referred as (585)
    A.  symptom realignment
    B.  symptom restructuring
    C.  symptom dissociation
    D.  symptom substitution

28. The basic concept of counterconditioning is to (589)
    A.  bring unconscious conflicts onto awareness to be dealt with
    B.  direct feelings at a therapist that are really for someone else
    C.  replace an undesired CR with a more appropriate one
    D.  remove the reinforcers that are maintaining a behavior

29. When children are in time out, it is important that they receive (588-589)
    A.  negative reinforcement for their behavior
    B.  no reinforcement at all for their behavior
    C.  token reinforcement for their behavior
    D.  positive reinforcement for their behavior

30. In systematic desensitization, the appropriate response that is being conditioned is (589)
    A.  a phobia
    B.  happiness
    C.  relaxation
    D.  insight

31. Which of the following involves dealing with psychological problems by changing the ways in which individuals think and act? (569)
    A.  behavioral medicine
    B.  biotherapy
    C.  psychiatry
    D.  psychotherapy

32. Systematic desensitization is primarily used in the treatment of (590)
    A.  schizophrenia
    B.  mood disorders
    C.  phobias and impulse control
    D.  somatoform disorders

33. Cognitive therapists believe that, for the most part, emotional disorders (593)
    A. have physical causes
    B. result from unconscious conflicts and motives
    C. result from environmental stimuli
    D. result from faulty thinking

34. How can client-centered therapy be best described? (582)
    A. ahistorical
    B. evaluative
    C. structured
    D. nondirective

35. Which therapy emphasizes the beliefs that thoughts affect behavior, that they can be monitored, and that changing thoughts will change behavior? (593)
    A. systematic desensitization
    B. cognitive restructuring
    C. aversive conditioning
    D. free association

36. How would a behavior therapist most likely define the problem of an individual who stutters? (584)
    A. stuttering
    B. low self-esteem
    C. cognitive dissonance
    D. unresolved conflict

37. A technique often used with young children is (589)
    A. time-out:
    B. systematic desensitization.
    C. aversive conditioning.
    D. psychoanalysis.

38. According to Beck's cognitive therapy, depression is caused by (594)
    A. a discrepancy between the self-concept and reality
    B. distorted thoughts that make a person feel worthless
    C. a chemical imbalance in the cerebral cortex
    D. unconscious conflicts created in early childhood

39. What is the primary aim of family therapy? (597-598)
    A. identify maladaptive behavior in family members.
    B. change the way the family interacts.
    C. restructure the organization of the family.
    D. balance the power in the family.

40. An antipsychotic drug is: (603)
    A. imipramine.
    B. benzodiazepine.
    C. barbiturates.
    D. chlorpromazine.

324

41. Meichenbaum's self-instructional therapy involves teaching clients to (594-595)
    A.   tell themselves what to do in many different situations
    B.   analyze their own dreams for their unconscious symbols
    C.   discuss their deepest inner needs more freely with others
    D.   give themselves rewards for behaving appropriately

42. A special form of group therapy in which all the members of the group have a special relationship and are committed to each other's well being is (597)
    A.   family therapy
    B.   an encounter group
    C.   social therapy
    D.   psychodrama

43. All of the following are biological therapies EXCEPT: (599)
    A.   electroconvulsive therapy
    B.   cognitive restructuring
    C.   drug therapy
    D.   psychosurgery

44. The most powerful antidepressant drugs, which require that patients stay on a strictly controlled diet, are (601)
    A.   tricyclics
    B.   MAO inhibitors
    C.   serotonin reuptake inhibitors
    D.   thymoleptics

45. Electroconvulsive shock therapy is used to treat (603)
    A.   catatonic schizophrenia
    B.   paranoid schizophrenia
    C.   anxiety disorders
    D.   severe depression

# When You Have Finished

## Essay Questions:

1.      Distinguish between the two types of insight theory and how they view individual's problems. (578, 581)

2.      Characterize behavior therapy and cognitive therapy and their differences. (583-585,593)

3.      Briefly describe the major types of drug therapy. (600-603)

4.      What is codependence and describe a person who is codependent (598)

5.      What is the placebo effect and what techniques are used to overcome it(569-570)

# Chapter 17

# Psychology in Action

## Before you read...

This chapter examines a multitude of fields in which psychology is applied to modern life. Industrial/Organizational psychology is divide into four broad areas: human resources, motivating job performance, job satisfaction, and leadership. Human resource psychologists work in the personnel area to select, train, promote, evaluate performance and determine benefits of employees.

Motivating people on the job requires a unique approach to understanding human behavior. Humans have desires more complex than basic needs. The goal-setting theory states that people given specific, clear, attainable goals will perform better. Expectancy theory asserts that goal-directed behavior is determined by expectancy of outcomes. Vroom adds that employees must first have willingness and ability. Others state that role perceptions play a role in job motivation. Equity theory states that if people are treated fairly compared to coworkers then they will be satisfied and perform well. Three basic approaches exist to managing motivation. The paternalistic approach is to take care of employees' needs in a fatherly fashion. The behavioral approach assumes people will work if they are rewarded. The participatory approach empowers people to become part of the organization.

Job satisfaction differs from job motivation. Motivation is the internal drive, and satisfaction is an attitude that may not be reflected in job behavior. Although factors that contribute to job satisfaction are numerous, they cluster into five general categories: the work itself, the rewards, supervision, coworker support, and the work setting. Leadership is an important contributor to job satisfaction and motivation. Two major theories that describe leadership effectiveness are the Fiedler contingency model and Vroom's leadership model. A description of a transformational leader is also provided.

Human factors psychologists are concerned with the relationship between humans and machines. Their goals are to provide efficiency and safety on the job.

Psychologists are providing assistance in the legal arena in a variety of ways. They are being employed as researchers, policy or program evaluators, advocates, and expert witnesses. Although psychologists and lawyers do not always agree, the psychologist is being recognized as a key player in both the private and public sector.

Environmental psychologists are interested in how the physical setting affects human behavior. Variables such as temperature, noise, toxins, and crowding are discussed. In the discussion on crowding, personal space, culture, and territoriality are examined. *Psychology* examines the role of environmental psychology in changing people's behaviors toward preservation of the environment.

Community psychology provides primary, secondary, and tertiary prevention programs to entire communities. Educational psychology combines instructional techniques and classroom management principles into working systems models for school settings. The relatively new field of sport psychology applies psychological principles such as motivation, an understanding of arousal and anxiety, and relaxation training to helping athletes maximize performance.

# Chapter Objectives

- Characterize the field of I/O psychology and describe its four broad areas: human resources psychology, motivation of job performance, job satisfaction, and leadership.
- Describe the personnel functions of human resource psychologists in the areas of job analysis, selection, training, and performance appraisal; explain the role of cognition in accurate performance appraisals.
- Identify the theories that explain job motivation and distinguish between job satisfaction and job motivation.
- Describe the results of recent studies on leadership.
- Describe how human factors psychologists are involved in helping people and machines work together more efficiently.
- Discuss the three categories of designs used to enhance the safety of the work environment.
- Describe the multiple roles that psychologists play in the legal system, as researchers, policy or program evaluators, advocates, and expert witnesses.
- Discuss how temperature, noise, and environmental toxins act as environmental stressors and have the potential to affect performance.
- Characterize the conditions that contribute to the psychological state of crowding and discuss the variations in needs for personal space and territoriality.
- Discuss the findings concerning how people can be encouraged to conserve natural resources and protect the environment.
- Discuss the general aims of community psychology, describe the key elements involved in efforts to bring about social change, and identify the three levels of prevention programs utilized by community psychologists.
- Characterize educational psychologists and discuss how research findings on time allocation, engaged time, classroom rules, and pacing help establish effective classroom management and instruction.
- Describe how sport psychology attempts to bring order to the study of athletic performance.
- List the four levels of analysis used to understand what motivates a person to perform well.
- Distinguish between arousal and anxiety, and describe some of the stress management techniques used to relieve anxiety and arousal while increasing athletic performance.

# As you read...

## Industrial/ Organizational Psychology

1.    Define Applied Psychology

2.    Define industrial/organizational psychology.

3.    How does culture affect I/O psychology?

4.    List and describe the 4 broad areas of I/O psychology.

| 17-1    Human Resources Psychology |
| --- |

5.    What is strategic planning?

6.    Define job analysis and its role in strategic planning.

7.    What are the 3 hierarchies of a functional job analysis?

8.    Describe the 6 major areas covered by the position analysis questionnaire.

9.    What is the basic goal of selection procedures?

10.    What are tests of general mental abilities?

11.    Tests that measure _____ are sometimes seen as controversial when determining the level of a candidate's integrity.

12.    Describe the results of Huffcutt and Roth's research on job interviews

13.    Describe some different types of training corporations use.

14. The problems that are often associated with performance appraisals when objective measures are used are _____, _____ _____, ____ _____ _____, and _____.

15. Define meta-analysis.

16. What are the conclusions of Davidson and Burke's research?

---

| 17-2 | **Motivation of Job Performance** |

17. What are the 4 dimensions that organizations and cultures vary on?

18. Define intrinsically motivated behavior.

19. What are SMART goals?

20. Describe the goal-setting theory.

21. Describe expectancy theory.

22. According to Vroom, the expectancy theory has three parts: _____, _____, and _____.

23. What are the key variables in determining performance?

24. Describe equity theory.

25. What are the 5 ways people alter inequalities?

26. Define self-efficacy and how it affects work performance.

27.    Describe the 3 basic motivation management approaches?

17-3    **Job Satisfaction**

28.    How is job satisfaction different than job motivation?

29.    What are the 5 basic categories of job satisfaction?

30.    How does team work effect job satisfaction?

17-4    **Leadership**

31.    Describe leaders and their goal.

32.    What problems are there with the trait theory of leadership?

33.    One defining trait of a effective leader is _____, the ability to quickly adapt to the ever changing environment.

34.    Describe employee-oriented and task-oriented leaders.

35.    How does gender effect leadership evaluation?

36.    Describe Vroom's leadership model.

37.    What are transformational leaders?

38.    What are the 7 guidelines to being an effective leader?

# Human Factors

1.      Define human factors.


2.      Human factors researchers seek to design interfaces between people and machines that maximize _____ ,minimize _____ and _____ , and are _____ .


3.      What are the differences between and I/O psychologist and a human factors psychologist?


4.      In order to design a effective interface, psychologists must study _____ , _____ _____ ,and complex _____ _____ .

5.      Define behavior-based safety and its goals.


6.      Describe a good safety culture.


7.      Describe the 3 categories of efforts to design safe work environments.


8.      How has research in perception and environmental research helped improved safety.


# Psychology and the Law

1.      Define legal psychology.


2.      What is forensic psychology?


3.      Define psychological jurisprudence.

4.	Psychologist that help institutions determine if policies, agencies or programs work are called _____ _____.


5.	What is an advocate?


6.	What is an expert witness?


7.	How has DNA changed the criminal system?


8.	What has research shown about the violent crime rate and the death penalty?


9.	Why is the alliance between lawyers and psychologists an uneasy one?


# Environmental Psychology

| 17-7 | Environmental Variables |
|------|-------------------------|

1.	Define environmental psychology.


2.	What is a stressor?


3.	How does high temperature affect behavior?


4.	How do different types of noise effect behavior?


5.	What are pollutants and how do they effect behavior?


| 17-8 | Crowding |
|------|----------|

6.	Define crowding.

7.   Distinguish between social and spatial density.

8.   Describe the Valins and Baum dormitory study.

9.   What universal effects are seen in high density situations?

10.  Define personal space.

11.  Hall defined four spatial zones in reference to personal space: _____ , _____ , _____ , and _____ _____ .

12.  Define privacy.

13.  Behaviors that establish, maintain and defend a delineated space are called _____ _____ .

| 17-9   Preserving the Environment |

14.  What things are most effective in getting people to adopt conservation behaviors?

15.  What does Geller suggest needs to be done to solve worldwide environmental problems?

## Community Psychology

1.   Is the internet adversely affecting social interactions?

2.   Define Community Psychology.

3.   What are the goals of community psychology?

4.   Define empowerment.

5.    List and describe the 3 levels of prevention.

6.    A _____ _____ was created in response to the growing need for a primary prevention service agency that targets mental health problems.

7.    _____ _____ _____ are centers which help people deal with short term situations that require immediate therapeutic counseling.

8.    How is self-esteem related to drinking?

9.    How can psychologist help decrease excessive drinking?

# Educational Psychology

10.    Define educational psychology.

11.    How are education and school psychologists different?

## 17-10   Problems Studied by Educational Psychologist

12.    Define Developmental change.

13.    What environmental conditions affect the learning process?

14.    What other factors do educational psychologists analyze?

## 17-11   Putting Theory Into Practice: Classroom Management

15.    What are some forms of punishment?

16.    List some ways time should be allocated in the classroom.

17.     Rules that are limited in number are more _____.

18.     What factors determine effective pacing?

# Sport Psychology

1.      Define sports psychology.

2.      What are the 3 main goals of the sports psychologist?

3.      How are sports psychologists trained?

## 17-12   Activation and Arousal in Athletic Performance

4.      Define arousal.

5.      How are arousal and performance related?

## 17-13   Anxiety and Sports Performance

6.      Define anxiety.

7.      How are anxiety and arousal related?

## 17-14   Intervention Strategies

8.      Describe progressive relaxation.

9.      How is hypnosis used with athletes?

10.    What is meditation?

11.    Define mental imagery.

12.    Describe cognitive interventions.

---

**17-15   How Do You Motivate Athletes?**

13.    What is the 4 step analysis to understanding what motivates a person?

14.    What other things do high achievers do?

---

**17-16   Sports Psychology: The Future**

15.    Describe the future of sports psychology.

Applied Psychology
Industrial/Organizational Psychology
Job Analyses
Performance Appraisal
Goal-Setting Theory
Expectancy Theories
Equity Theory
Transformational Leader
Human Factors

Environmental Psychology
Crowding
Personal Space
Privacy
Territorial Behavior
Community Psychology
Empowerment
Educational Psychology
Sports Psychology

# After you read . . . Self Test

## Chapter 17 Self Test:

1.  The branch of psychology that uses psychological principles to help solve the problems of everyday living is called (608)
    A.   general psychology
    B.   everyday psychology
    C.   applied psychology
    D.   organizational psychology

2.  The study of how worker's behaviors is affected by the work environment, by coworkers, and by organizational practices is called (608)
    A.   collective/productive psychology
    B.   union/management psychology
    C.   economic/managerial psychology
    D.   industrial/organizational psychology

3.  People are motivated to work productively *primarily* through: (616)
    A.   receiving monetary rewards.
    B.   the social affiliation that comes with a job.
    C.   having feelings of self-worth.
    D.   a variety and unique combination of physiological and social needs being fulfilled.

4.  According to Vroom's expectancy theory, people are motivated by: (616-617)
    A.   doing what they are expected to do.
    B.   what they expect to get from performing an assigned task.
    C.   having the ability to make an assigned task a rewarding experience.
    D.   B and C

5.  The main reason why companies in different countries are organized in different ways is that they _____. (609)
    A.   have less business experience than U.S. companies
    B.   must obey a different set of national business laws

    C.   are less motivated to be successful than U.S. companies
    D.   reflect the nature of the society they are a part of

6.  Job satisfaction: (620)
    A.   is a person's attitude about his or her job.
    B.   is directly related to job performance.
    C.   is solely determined by one's ability to do the job.
    D.   A and B

7. Most psychologists see the paternalistic management style as being self-defeating because this style: (618)
    A. prevents slower workers from receiving rewards.
    B. prevents employees from having any influence in establishing goals for the company.
    C. does not encourage hard work because rewards are given without contingency.
    D. requires hard work without adequate rewards.

8. Employees tend to experience a sense of self-determination and competence when they work under: (619)
    A. behavioral management styles.
    B. participatory management styles.
    C. boss-centered leadership.
    D. task-oriented leadership styles.

9. Selecting people for a job, determining benefits packages, and developing job training programs are all important functions for _____ psychologists (609)
    A. strategic
    B. human resources
    C. employment analysis
    D. forensic

10. What is probably the most important goal of industrial/organizational psychology in the United States (608)
    A. stimulate the motivation of workers.
    B. increase productivity
    C. reduce the cost of labor
    D. provide a pleasant environment for workers

11. According to Lawler and Porter, job performance is determined by: (617)
    A. motivation, ability, and role perception.
    B. personal, social, and environmental factors.
    C. skill, incentives, and perceived status.
    D. intrinsic rewards, social comparison, and achievement motivation.

12. Which of the following situations is likely in an organization that has paternalistic management? (618)
    A. Workers compete for challenging jobs.
    B. Bosses socialize with workers.
    C. Workers take pride in the product they produce.
    D. Pay is based on length of service.

13. Susan is paid by the number of boxes of apples she picks. This is an example of the _____ approach to motivating workers. (618)
    A. behavioral
    B. traditional
    C. participatory
    D. extrinsic

14. In which type management would you most likely find "quality circles?" (619)
    A.  paternalistic
    B.  egalitarian
    C.  interactive
    D.  participatory

15. An environmental psychologist probably *would* not: (631)
    A.  be conducting all his research in a laboratory.
    B.  investigate behaviors like cognitive dissonance or group polarization.
    C.  focus on applied problems and their solutions.
    D.  be interested in how humans make changes in their environment.

16. Research investigating the effects of temperature shifts on performance indicate that when temperatures become uncomfortably high: (632)
    A.  experimental subjects become more willing to administer shock to other subjects.
    B.  people become more concerned with their own discomfort than with performance or goal-oriented activity.
    C.  adaptive behaviors counteract the effects of the temperature.
    D.  people show more aggression.

17. If a psychologist observes a group of 100 people in a 1,000 square foot room and then moves the group to a 10,000 square foot room and observes them there, he is studying the effects of: (633)
    A.  crowding.
    B.  social density.
    C.  spatial density.
    D.  social and spatial density.

18. The spatial zone that Hall called social distance: (636)
    A.  is usually maintained by using some kind of physical barrier.
    B.  allows good eye contact and a sense of being personal.
    C.  is commonly found in contact sports.
    D.  eliminates personal communication between individuals.

19. When an organization's highest management develops long-term goals and determines how best to achieve those goals, it is called (609)
    A.  job analysis
    B.  collective bargaining
    C.  strategic planning
    D.  human resources

20. The most recent concern of environmental psychologists is the study of: (637)
    A.  how natural environments affect behavior.
    B.  how man-made environments affect behavior.
    C.  how behavior affects the environment.
    D.  development of lifelong behaviors that will help maintain environmental quality.

21. A detailed description of the tasks that will be required for employees to do a job, the resources and skills they will need, and how they will be evaluated is called a  (609-610)
    A.  strategic plan
    B.  screening test
    C.  job analysis
    D.  motivational system

22. A functional job analysis (FJA) specifies three hierarchies for worker functions for each job. These hierarchies relate to (610)
    A.  superiors, peers, and subordinates
    B.  preparation, performance, and evaluation
    C.  employment, promotion, and compensation
    D.  information, people, and things

23. A position analysis questionnaire is widely used to get information from workers about (610)
    A.  how they like their jobs and the companies they work for
    B.  what changes would make their jobs easier or more pleasant
    C.  what positions might be open in their organization soon
    D.  the skills, activities and resources that their jobs require

24. Firefighter students have to pass a state proficiency test involving physical skills such as carrying a body, hooking up hoses, and setting up ladders. This is best described as (611)
    A.  an intelligence test
    B.  a work sample test
    C.  a handwriting test
    D.  a test on integrity

25. Which of the following tests might be used to test integrity? (611)
    A.  WAIS intelligence test
    B.  Scholastic Aptitude Test
    C.  a work sample test
    D.  MMPI-2 personality test

26. The best way to reduce the effect of bias against minorities in interviews is (612)
    A.  to have a highly structured interview
    B.  probe for negative information in minority applicants' backgrounds
    C.  reduce the size of the pool of applicants
    D.  rely on ability tests scores to set a standard for comparing applicants

27. One of the most effective methods of training a new employee for a job is to have this person (612-613)
    A.  watch training videos produced by the management
    B.  ask questions whenever something isn't clear
    C.  observe and interact with a more senior employee
    D.  attend lectures on organization procedures and rules

28. The process by which a supervisor or employer periodically evaluates how well an employee is doing on the job is called a(n) (613)
    A. job analysis
    B. performance appraisal
    C. employment review
    D. worker evaluation

29. Samantha's manager is very understanding when she needs time off for family matters; Lian's manager marks her down for this on her performance ratings. These managers clearly differ in their (614)
    A. halo effect
    B. leniency
    C. reliability
    D. effectiveness

30. In Hefsted's analysis of companies all over the world, a company that emphasizes the importance of getting the work done and puts less emphasis on relationships between co-workers demonstrates the value he called (615)
    A. individualism
    B. masculinity
    C. collectivism
    D. femininity

31. Goal-setting theory says that better performance will result when we set goals that are (616)
    A. specific, clear and attainable
    B. general enough to apply to everyone
    C. too hard for anyone to reach
    D. so easy there is no possible failure

32. Equity theory on the workplace emphasizes the importance of an employee's perception of (617)
    A. how much managers are paid compared to laborers
    B. the balance between what they put in and their benefits
    C. what others in the company think of their performance
    D. how well the company does compared to other companies

33. A company that wants to increase workers sense of self-efficacy should do all of the following EXCEPT (618)
    A. increase task complexity to increase intrinsic motivation
    B. provide accurate descriptions of work to be accomplishes
    C. suggest techniques to accomplish carious tasks
    D. increase the number of sub-goals for which a worker is paid

34. Someone who influences the behavior of others toward attaining an agreed-upon goal is called a (621)
    A. colleague
    B. supervisor
    C. manager
    D. leader

35. A key trait that seems to be common to most good leaders is (622)
    A. flexibility
    B. self-confidence
    C. sociability
    D. assertiveness

36. A leader who focuses on enhancing workers' self- worth is _____ oriented; one who focuses on getting the job done effectively is _____ oriented (622)
    A. satisfaction; motivation
    B. motivation; satisfaction
    C. task; employee
    D. employee; task

37. The study of how humans interact with machines and workplaces in an attempt to make these things more usable and safer is called (625)
    A. industrial psychology
    B. robotics
    C. human factors
    D. engineering analysis

38. A workplace environment in which a certain type of error is less likely to happen, but still might happen, exhibits a(n) design (627)
    A. prevention
    B. exclusion
    C. fail-safe
    D. inclusion

39. The application of psychological principles to phenomena or issues on the legal system is known as (627-628)
    A. psychology jurisprudence
    B. forensic psychology
    C. legal psychology
    D. psycholegal research

40. As researcher, psychologist may participate in the legal system by (628)
    A. determining whether a specific person is mentally competent
    B. explaining details of psychological tests to jurors and judges
    C. measuring the personality trait of an accused criminal
    D. studying the causes and treatment for aggressive behaviors

41. As evaluators Psychologists may participate in the legal system by (628)
    A.   determining whether a particular program actually works
    B.   studying factors that cause people to become criminals
    C.   measuring the competence of prison guards and wardens
    D.   assessing the mental competence of an accused criminal

42. When a noise interferes with our ability to communicate, when it raises physiological arousal, or is so loud that it causes pain, then the noise is likely to become a(n) (632)
    A.   pollutant
    B.   stimulus
    C.   depressant
    D.   stressor

43. How do environmental psychologists define crowding? (633)
    A.   in terms of volume of space per person
    B.   as a situational variable
    C.   as a psychological state
    D.   in terms of area of floor space per person

44. The area around a person that the person considers private and defends from other people is called (635)
    A.   personal space
    B.   social density
    C.   crowd limitation
    D.   spatial density

45. When two friends are standing together and talking at a party, with about 2 feet of space between them, they are maintaining a(n) distance (635-636)
    A.   public
    B.   social
    C.   personal
    D.   intimate

# When You Have Finished

## Essay Questions:

1.    What are the 4 broad areas of I/O psychology and how does each area help corporations succeed? (609)

2.    How does psychology interact with the law? (628-629)

3.    What are the 3 levels of prevention? Give an example of each. (639-640)

4.    Describe the 3 main areas of work of sports psychologists (644)

5.    What are the 3 classroom management techniques and how does each affect classroom effectiveness? (642-643)

# GRADE AID

# ANSWER SECTION

## CHAPTER ONE

**SELF TEST ANSWERS**

| 1 | C | 16 | A | 31 | A |
|---|---|----|---|----|---|
| 2 | D | 17 | D | 32 | A |
| 3 | A | 18 | A | 33 | D |
| 4 | C | 19 | B | 34 | B |
| 5 | B | 20 | C | 35 | A |
| 6 | A | 21 | C | 36 | A |
| 7 | B | 22 | B | 37 | A |
| 8 | D | 23 | C | 38 | C |
| 9 | B | 24 | B | 39 | B |
| 10 | A | 25 | D | 40 | B |
| 11 | B | 26 | B | 41 | D |
| 12 | B | 27 | D | 42 | D |
| 13 | B | 28 | A | 43 | A |
| 14 | A | 29 | C | 44 | A |
| 15 | D | 30 | A | 45 | D |

**ESSAY QUESTIONS**

1. An independent variable is the variable that is manipulated to in order to see what change occurs as a result. The dependant variable is what is expected to change as a result of the manipulation; it is the variable that is measured. For this experiment, the culture of the subject would be the independent variable since it is what is expected to impact the dependant variable of alcohol consumption.

2. The book discusses three early schools of thought, structuralism, functionalism and Gestalt psychology. Structuralism was the school of thought that focused on the structure and elements of the immediate, conscious experience. They believe that all conscious experiences could be broken down into simple elements. Edward Titchener was the man responsible for brining structuralism to the United States. Functionalism included part of structuralism; they focused not just on the structures of the mind but also wanted to know how the mind functions in relation to consciousness. Additionally, functionalism looked at how people adapt to their environment. William James headed the functionalism movement. Max Wertheimer and Kurt Koffka believed that in order to study conscious experiences you need to look at the total experience, not just the parts of the mind or behavior. This reflects the Gestalt psychology school of thought. Gestalt psychology also used perceptual frameworks as a way of explaining how each individual molds sensory information into unique experiences.

3. A behaviorist would say that the person has been conditioned to eat at noon. In the behaviorists perspective the time of day, noon, has become a stimulus that elicits a behavior, eating, and that this response has been conditioned such that when the time is noon the person eats. The cognitive psychologist would concentrate on the persons ideas and thoughts, not the stimuli and responses. In order to determine why the person ate at noon everyday they would ask the person what they were thinking, and how they thought about lunch. Eating at noon would not be the result of it being noon, but some thought process the person was experiencing.

4. In conducting animal research, researchers are able to study things they could not study directly in humans. The human environment cannot be controlled as effectively as the animal's environment, allowing the researcher to isolate the behaviors and their causes from other variables. Also, the short life-span of animals allows researchers to study the entire life history of several generations in a short period of time. Animal rights activists believe that research is cruel to these animals and that these animals are not necessarily inferior to humans. They also point out that although similar in some respects to humans, each species responds differently to manipulations and therefore animal research may not be telling us anything about humans.

5. The psychiatrist would likely take a more medial approach to the depression and assume there was some biological cause for the depression and would likely start the person on an anti-depressant drug. The clinical psychologist would look at emotional and social causes for the depression and would try to treat the patient with some form of therapy. Similarly, the psychiatrist may conduct therapy with the patient in addition to the drug therapy. Also, the clinical psychologist may refer the client to a psychiatrist for drug therapy in addition to the therapy they are doing.

---

## CHAPTER TWO

**SELF TEST**

| | | | | | |
|----|----|----|----|----|----|
| 1 | B | 16 | D | 31 | D |
| 2 | D | 17 | C | 32 | C |
| 3 | A | 18 | D | 33 | B |
| 4 | A | 19 | B | 34 | D |
| 5 | C | 20 | D | 35 | B |
| 6 | C | 21 | A | 36 | C |
| 7 | B | 22 | B | 37 | B |
| 8 | B | 23 | A | 38 | D |
| 9 | C | 24 | C | 39 | C |
| 10 | A | 25 | C | 40 | C |
| 11 | C | 26 | B | 41 | D |
| 12 | B | 27 | A | 42 | C |
| 13 | C | 28 | D | 43 | B |
| 14 | D | 29 | C | 44 | D |
| 15 | D | 30 | A | 45 | D |

**ESSAY QUESTIONS**

1. The action potential of a neuron is reached when the neuron is stimulated to its threshold. The "gates of the cell membrane open making it permeable and potivit ions enter the neuron causing the neuron to be depolarized. The action potential itself is an electrical current that travels down the axon of the neuron. This firing occurs in an all-or-none fashion, it always occurs at full strength. After a neuron fires, there is a period of time, called a refractory period in which it cannot fire.

2. The human genome is the total DNA blueprint of heritable traits. In mapping the human genome, researchers gain better knowledge of basic human genetics and biological processes. It also has helped in finding the genes for many diseases. As we understand more about the genome, the more we can find cures for some genetic diseases.

3. Psychopharmocology is the study of how drugs affect behavior. Currently much of its research is focused on the level of the brain and the neurons. Research focuses on how certain drugs affect the neurotransmitters in the brain and how this in turn affects behavior. Some drugs are agonists and act just like the normally occurring neurotransmitter, other drugs are antagonists and block the actions of neurotransmitters.

4. Behavioral determinism is the idea that evolutionary history determines behavior and that this behavior cannot be altered. The fact that the brain has the ability to reorganize itself into adulthood is one piece of evidence against behavioral

---

determinism. The fact that culture and the environment impact behavior is another piece of evidence against it.

5. During the fight-or-flight state, the adrenal gland is stimulated by the sympathetic nervous system. The adrenal gland produces epinephrine producing a burst of energy. This in turn affects the somatic nervous system so that muscles can respond strongly and rapidly to the fight-or-flight situation.

## CHAPTER THREE

**SELF TEST**

| 1 | B | 16 | B | 31 | B |
|----|---|----|---|----|---|
| 2 | B | 17 | C | 32 | D |
| 3 | D | 18 | D | 33 | A |
| 4 | A | 19 | B | 34 | C |
| 5 | B | 20 | D | 35 | D |
| 6 | C | 21 | A | 36 | C |
| 7 | C | 22 | C | 37 | D |
| 8 | B | 23 | D | 38 | A |
| 9 | C | 24 | B | 39 | B |
| 10 | C | 25 | C | 40 | A |
| 11 | B | 26 | D | 41 | D |
| 12 | A | 27 | B | 42 | A |
| 13 | D | 28 | B | 43 | C |
| 14 | D | 29 | D | 44 | B |
| 15 | C | 30 | B | 45 | C |

**ESSAY QUESTIONS**

1. Cross-sectional designs use different people at different ages and measure their differences on some dimension. Longitudinal studies use the same people at different time points to look for changes on some dimension. Cross-sectional studies take less time and is less expensive. The problem with cross-sectional designs includes that you cannot control people's backgrounds, so differences may be due to the different backgrounds of your sample, not just the dimension you are measuring. Longitudinal studies helps control for background differences, but subjects may not be available at all time points, people move away, stop participating or may even die. Also, practice effects may cause problems for some longitudinal research.

2. Assimilation is the process of integrating new information into already existing mental structures and behaviors. Accommodation is the process of adapting current mental structures to account for new information or experiences. People continue to add, or assimilate new information into their established mental structures until it requires a new mental structure to accommodate the differences in the information they have assimilated.

3. A child at level one, preconventional morality, would reason that the wife should not have killed her husband because she might get punished for doing so. A child at level 2, conventional morality, would say the wife should not have killed her

husband because murder is against the law. A child at level 3, postconventional morality, would agree that killing her husband was illegal, but would determine if she should be punished based on their own values and how her act effects society and the community.

4. Theory of mind is the understanding that people have feelings, desires, beliefs and intentions that these have a causal role in human behavior. Theory of mind develops around the age of 3, but it develops out of the child's social activities. Interaction with family and those that involve how the culture the child is raised in sees and talks about people relate to each other and their world are important. Theory of mind is developed in all cultures but at different rates.

5. A father's involvement in childrearing is impacted by many factors including his work schedule and personal dispositions. More influential than either of thess factors is the attitude of the child's mother. If the mother supports the father's involvement the other factors become important, but if she does not the father is unlikely to be involved regardless of his work schedule and disposition. Culture is also a factor in the father's involvement.

## CHAPTER FOUR

**SELF TEST**

| 1 | D | 16 | B | 31 | D |
|----|---|----|---|----|---|
| 2 | D | 17 | B | 32 | B |
| 3 | B | 18 | A | 33 | C |
| 4 | C | 19 | C | 34 | C |
| 5 | D | 20 | C | 35 | A |
| 6 | C | 21 | B | 36 | B |
| 7 | B | 22 | C | 37 | D |
| 8 | D | 23 | B | 38 | A |
| 9 | A | 24 | C | 39 | B |
| 10 | A | 25 | D | 40 | D |
| 11 | B | 26 | D | 41 | D |
| 12 | B | 27 | A | 42 | D |
| 13 | C | 28 | B | 43 | B |
| 14 | C | 29 | D | 44 | B |
| 15 | A | 30 | B | 45 | A |

**ESSAY QUESTIONS**

1. Anorexia is characterized by a willful refusal to eat. People with the disorder have a distorted body image and perceive themselves as fat is they have deviate from their ideal body image. They have a relentless pursuit of being thin and this may cause permanent damage to their heart muscle tissue. The cause of anorexia is believed to mainly be psychological, but there may be physiological contributions such as a lack of hormone that makes them feel full. Bulimia is characterized by binge eating followed by purging. Fear of gaining weight from the binge eating causes bulimics to purge their system of the calories mostly by vomiting or taking laxatives and diuretics. Bulimia also has both psychological and biological contributors.

2. The imaginary audience and personal fable are two cognitive distortions that occur as the result of adolescence becoming egocentric. The imaginary audience is characterized by adolescences feeling that they are always on stage and that everyone is watching them all the time. This often causes behaviors designed to not call attention to themselves. The personal fable is a belief in which the adolescent thinks they are so unique that no one understands them and that bad things will not happen to them. This cognitive distortion often leads to risky behaviors, like unsafe sex.

3. The basic difference between Erickson and Levinson's theory is that Levinson believes that people are not all working toward the same specific goal. Levinson does think people go through stages, and have developmental tasks to work through but that these tasks are not the same for every individual and that they do not lead to a specific end. Levinson also focuses on the eras in which people work out their developmental tasks

4. Friendships are important for the development of social skills. This is evidenced by research by Hartup and Stevens that shows more social competence in children and adolescents that have friends. Friendships also prepare children for intimacy as adults. Friendship is also important in adulthood as a cognitive and emotional resource.

5. The cognitive changes that occur after age 65 include decreases in vocabulary. reaction time, mathematic ability, and memory. These decreases are often minor and are less noticeable in people who are cognitively active. Also, these changes can be overcome through cognitive interventions. The cognitive changes that occur after age 65 do not have a large impact on elderly people because the changes are small and those that do occur can be overcome.

## CHAPTER FIVE

**SELF TEST**

| | | | | | |
|---|---|---|---|---|---|
| 1 | D | 16 | B | 31 | A |
| 2 | D | 17 | C | 32 | C |
| 3 | C | 18 | A | 33 | D |
| 4 | A | 19 | C | 34 | B |
| 5 | A | 20 | C | 35 | A |
| 6 | B | 21 | B | 36 | D |
| 7 | B | 22 | C | 37 | A |
| 8 | B | 23 | D | 38 | D |
| 9 | C | 24 | B | 39 | C |
| 10 | A | 25 | D | 40 | A |
| 11 | A | 26 | A | 41 | D |
| 12 | D | 27 | B | 42 | B |
| 13 | B | 28 | A | 43 | A |
| 14 | A | 29 | A | 44 | B |
| 15 | C | 30 | B | 45 | D |

**ESSAY QUESTIONS**

1. Bottom-up analysis starts at the most fundamental level of sensation. This approach starts at the receptor and moves up toward the more complex processes of interpretation. Top-down analysis starts at the more complex processes and focuses on the perceptual process such as selective attention.

2. Taste is not only the chemical stimulation but is also influenced by the frequency and intensity of past experience, the amount of saliva produced and how long you chew. Texture also effects taste. Smells are also impacted by the frequency and intensity of our past experiences. It can also be influenced by language and emotional states of the person.

3. The evolutionary perspective asserts that the gender differences in spatial abilities developed due to the different tasks of men and women. Men as hunters developed spatial skills, while gathering fostered spatial memory in women. These differences in ability were selected for and may also explain why men and women use different strategies for navigating their way in the world. The fact that men and women navigate equally well in spite of these differences in strategies casts some doubts on the evolutionary perspective.

4. When told nothing, college students put into a dorm room experienced decreases in mental performance, became irritable and hallucinated. When another set of students were put into the same situation but were told before hand that sensory

deprivation would aid in mediation, they did not hallucinate or become irritable. Also, their mental abilities improved. This research illuminates the importance in a person's expectations and how those expectations can impact perception and experiences.

5. Prosopagnosia is the inability to recognize faces. Research on patients with this form of agnosia has demonstrated that certain brain cells are only activated by facial stimuli. Other cells have been found that respond best to faces. This does not mean there is a neuron for every face. Taking all prosopagnosia research as a whole paints a picture of a interacting and interdependent parts that create the whole visual experience.

## CHAPTER SIX

**SELF TEST**

| 1 | D | 16 | C | 31 | B |
|---|---|----|---|----|---|
| 2 | A | 17 | A | 32 | D |
| 3 | A | 18 | D | 33 | D |
| 4 | C | 19 | B | 34 | D |
| 5 | B | 20 | A | 35 | C |
| 6 | C | 21 | A | 36 | D |
| 7 | D | 22 | C | 37 | B |
| 8 | B | 23 | B | 38 | D |
| 9 | D | 24 | A | 39 | C |
| 10 | B | 25 | C | 40 | B |
| 11 | D | 26 | A | 41 | C |
| 12 | D | 27 | A | 42 | C |
| 13 | C | 28 | C | 43 | C |
| 14 | D | 29 | C | 44 | B |
| 15 | A | 30 | A | 45 | C |

**ESSAY QUESTIONS**

1. Sleep patterns and sleeping arrangements of different cultures are different. In tribal cultures, sleeping arrangements are in groups and do not normally include mattresses. Noise is also a common factor during sleep time in these cultures. Also people in different cultures have different amounts of each stage of sleep although they do have the same 5 stages. In tribal cultures there people spend less time in the deeper stages of 3 and 4.

2. Dopamine is a neurotransmitter that is involved in the experience of all types of pleasurable stimulation and the brain's "reward system". Most drugs affect dopamine in some way. Cocaine stops the reuptake of dopamine, there by leaving more of it available in the synapse thereby allowing dopamine to have a longer affect. Amphetamines cause more dopamine to be released thereby increasing the duration of dopamine's effect. Due to the increased effects of the dopamine, drugs become associated with pleasurable emotions. Repeated exposure to drugs causes the brain to be primed for the effects of drugs and can contribute to addiction.

3. Research has shown that life events affect dream content. Children living in violent societies have dreams that contain more persecution and aggression than those living in less violent societies. Although life events influence dreams,

culture has not been shown to. Cultures with similar amounts of violence did not show differences in the content of children's dreams.

4. Substance abuse is evidenced by use for over one month; legal, personal, social or vocation problems that are the result of use, and use even when doing so is hazardous. Withdrawal symptoms are the physical reactions that occur when person that has become dependant on some substance stops taking that substance. Withdrawal symptoms are different for every drug and are usually the opposite of the drug's effect.

5. Sleepwalking occurs during stage 4 of the sleep cycle. The brain activity of sleepwalkers shows different levels of activity across the brain. The motor portions of the brain sow high activity, while the areas of the brain responsible for higher-level cognitive process show very little activity. Sleepwalking is normally seen in children and is seen more often in boys than girls. Most children stop sleepwalking as they get older.

## CHAPTER SEVEN

**SELF TEST**

| 1 | D | 16 | D | 31 | D |
|---|---|----|---|----|---|
| 2 | D | 17 | D | 32 | C |
| 3 | A | 18 | C | 33 | A |
| 4 | A | 19 | B | 34 | B |
| 5 | D | 20 | A | 35 | A |
| 6 | C | 21 | C | 36 | C |
| 7 | B | 22 | B | 37 | A |
| 8 | D | 23 | C | 38 | B |
| 9 | C | 24 | D | 39 | B |
| 10 | B | 25 | B | 40 | C |
| 11 | B | 26 | A | 41 | C |
| 12 | D | 27 | B | 42 | D |
| 13 | A | 28 | B | 43 | D |
| 14 | C | 29 | C | 44 | D |
| 15 | C | 30 | B | 45 | B |

**ESSAY QUESTIONS**

1. Allergies can be classically conditioned. Pet dander is the unconditioned stimulus for many people, this elicits an allergic reaction. If every time you go to a friend's house you have an allergic reaction due to the dog at their house, you can be conditioned to have the allergic reaction. Even if your friend gets rid of the animal you will still have allergic reactions because of the classical conditioning. The immune system of animals has been classically conditioned in the same way. These animals bodies released antibodies in reaction to the conditioned stimulus of sweetened water after it had been paired with a toxin.

2. The main difference between negative reinforcement and punishment is their goals; negative reinforcement is used to increase behavior while punishment is used to decrease behavior. Negative reinforcement is used to increase a behavior by the removal of an aversive stimulus. Punishment is used to decrease a behavior by the presentation of an aversive stimulus or the removal of a desired stimulus.

3. Hebb proposed that groups of neurons work together to form a recurring pattern. He termed this network of neurons a reverberating circuit. When learning takes place stimulation of a set of neurons occurs. With repeated stimulation, these neurons form a permanent circuit, referred to as consolidation. Differences in the

ability of the neurons to consolidate maybe the reason for different learning abilities.

4.  Children often imitate what they see. Research has shown that this imitation also includes imitation of physical aggression. If a parent physically punishes their children, the child is likely to imitate that physical aggression. Children may direct this physical aggression at the punisher in an attempt to stop the punishment. Also, people who are punished often display aggression and hostility toward members of their group.

5.  Avoidance conditioning involves learning some behavior to avoid some undesirable stimulus. The process of avoidance conditioning involves escape learning, ie press the bar to escape shock, and then pressing the bar to a signal to keep the shock from ever occurring. Learning to respond in order to never receive the undesirable stimulus can be adaptive. For example, cleaning your room before your mother comes home, to avoid punishment. It can also explain maladaptive behaviors in the case of irrational fears where the person avoids the situation all together.

---

## CHAPTER EIGHT

**SELF TEST**

| | | | | | |
|---|---|---|---|---|---|
| 1 | B | 16 | C | 31 | D |
| 2 | D | 17 | D | 32 | B |
| 3 | C | 18 | D | 33 | B |
| 4 | D | 19 | B | 34 | A |
| 5 | B | 20 | C | 35 | B |
| 6 | A | 21 | A | 36 | A |
| 7 | D | 22 | C | 37 | C |
| 8 | D | 23 | B | 38 | B |
| 9 | C | 24 | D | 39 | D |
| 10 | A | 25 | A | 40 | B |
| 11 | C | 26 | C | 41 | C |
| 12 | A | 27 | C | 42 | D |
| 13 | C | 28 | A | 43 | B |
| 14 | B | 29 | B | 44 | C |
| 15 | A | 30 | A | 45 | C |

**ESSAY QUESTIONS**

1. Medial temporal lobe including the hippocampus important in long-term memory formation. Storage is distributed over the entire cerebral cortex and even lower brain structures. Retrieval activates pathways in prefrontal cortex and medial temporal lobes.

2. Declarative memory is for specifc information. Procedural is memory for skills. Declarative memory can be broken down into episodic and semantic memories. Episodic memory is memory of specific personal events and is tagged with information about time. Autobiographical memory is episodic memory of your own story. Semantic memory is memory for ideas, rules, words and general concepts.

3. Maintenance rehearsal is repetitive with no interpretations. Elaborative involves repetition and analysis, further processing and is more effective than maintenance rehearsal. Practice comes in two forms, distribution and massed. Distribution is more effective for learning and retention. Therefore studying should be distributed over different times, not cramming for the test and should involve analysis and deeper level processing.

4. Baddley and Longman looked at the effects of massed and distributed practice. Massed practice is where the subject practices intensively at one time, distributed practice breaks the practice session into several intervals. Baddley and Longman's study looked at the effects of the different types of practice on typing. Their results indicate that subjects who had practice sessions over several days, that is distributed

---

practice had better performance than those with massed practice. Since all subjects had the same total hours of practice. this indicates that distributed practice is more effective.

5. False memories are memories for information or events that did not actually occur. Therapists who use suggestive techniques, such as hypnosis on their patients, can create false memories. These false memories are usually related to trauma and repressed memories. Normal memory processes can also create false memories. If you remember a word as being on the list, and it in fact was not, you have experienced a false memory. This type of false memory is not the result of repression or suggestion by someone else, it is simply the result of typical memory processes.

# CHAPTER NINE

**SELF TEST**

| | | | | | |
|----|---|----|---|----|---|
| 1  | B | 16 | D | 31 | A |
| 2  | D | 17 | D | 32 | B |
| 3  | A | 18 | B | 33 | C |
| 4  | D | 19 | A | 34 | A |
| 5  | C | 20 | D | 35 | D |
| 6  | D | 21 | C | 36 | A |
| 7  | A | 22 | C | 37 | B |
| 8  | B | 23 | A | 38 | C |
| 9  | D | 24 | C | 39 | A |
| 10 | B | 25 | D | 40 | A |
| 11 | A | 26 | A | 41 | B |
| 12 | C | 27 | B | 42 | C |
| 13 | B | 28 | C | 43 | A |
| 14 | C | 29 | A | 44 | D |
| 15 | C | 30 | D | 45 | A |

**ESSAY QUESTIONS**

1. Concept formation is the way people organize and classify events and objects, usually to solve problems. Exemplars are specific instances of a concept. Fuzzy concepts exists when the concept is not clear cut as often happens. People tend to use prototypes, an idealized abstraction of the concept, to decide if a new stimulus is part of the concept.

2. Neural networks learn and remember by altering the weights or values associated with various connections. A unit that is activated more frequently forms a stronger connection and becomes more easily activated in the future. Easier activation leads to easier retrieval.

3. Chomsky proposed that language is innate to humans. What he proposed was innate was a universal grammar for sounds to be words to be sentences. Infant research shows that infants respond physiologically to language. Research with deaf children also support the idea that language is innate. Brown's naturalistic observations of children also support the idea that there is an innate basis for language acquisition.

4. Creative ideas are original, novel, and appropriate. Original ideas are those that are not imitations of some other idea, and come directly from the problem solver. Novel ideas are those ideas that do not have a precedent and that are new. Appropriate responses are those that are reasonable solutions to the

problem and the given situation. Creative ideas break out of the mental set of the person and can be very effective in problem solving.

5. Language and culture interact. A belief that is held in a specific culture is often reflected in the language of that culture. Research with people who are bilingual has shown that how a person responds to personality tests depends on the language in which the test is written. Subjects will give answers that are more consistent with the values of the culture of the language of the test. If given the same test in a different language their responses will reflect the values of the culture of the second language.

## CHAPTER TEN

**SELF TEST**

| 1 | B | 16 | B | 31 | C |
|---|---|----|---|----|---|
| 2 | D | 17 | C | 32 | C |
| 3 | C | 18 | B | 33 | C |
| 4 | B | 19 | A | 34 | B |
| 5 | D | 20 | D | 35 | A |
| 6 | C | 21 | C | 36 | B |
| 7 | B | 22 | A | 37 | C |
| 8 | C | 23 | A | 38 | D |
| 9 | A | 24 | C | 39 | B |
| 10 | B | 25 | B | 40 | D |
| 11 | D | 26 | D | 41 | C |
| 12 | B | 27 | D | 42 | A |
| 13 | D | 28 | B | 43 | |
| 14 | C | 29 | A | 44 | |
| 15 | D | 30 | A | 45 | |

**ESSAY QUESTIONS**

1. Reliability is a tests ability to return the same score when the test is administered to the same person twice. If a test is not reliable, then it is context dependant and is not an accurate measure. Validity is the tests ability to measure exactly what it was designed to measure. If the test is not valid then the results cannot be used as a measure of the quality, trait or ability it was designed to measure. Without both reliability and validity a test is not useful for its designated purpose.

2. There are 3 different Wechsler Scales, the WAIS, WISC and WPPSI, each one of these is administered to a different age group, adults, children age 6-16 and children age 4 – 6 _ respectively. This is the major advantage the Weschler Scales have over the Stanford-Binet which does not work well with adults. The subscales of the Weschler Scales are grouped by content, such that all math questions are presented together. Each subtest is converted to a standard score so that comparisons across ages can be made.

3. A deprived environment, such as one lacking in nutrition and cognitive stimulation may lead to retardation. This normally leads to mild retardation. Infectious diseases and physical trauma such as alcohol or drug use can also lead to mental retardation. Finally, genetic causes such as Down syndrome and fragile X can also lead to mental retardation.

4. People with different cognitive abilities can have the same or different emotional intelligence. According to Goleman, if two people with the same cognitive abilities have different emotional intellignce the one with the higher emotional intelligence will do better than the one with the lower emotional intelligence. People with high emotional intelligence will be able to manage life and its difficulties better regardless of cognitive abilities. Further, it is proposed that those with higher emotional intelligence will better harness their intellectual capabilities.

5. One criticism of IQ test scores is that they are more reflective of the subject's motivation to succeed than it is of their actual intelligence. Two children of the same intelligence, but with different levels of motivation to succeed may score differently on the tests. Stereotype threat is another criticism of IQ scores. Stereotype threat is the fear of being reduced to a stereotype. Steele contends that minorities, when focusing on scholastic task, fear confirming a negative bias and that this fear impacts their scores. Defenders of IQ scores say that the tests themselves do not impact motivation and attitudes, but they do admit that attitudes and motivation are important factors.

## CHAPTER ELEVEN

**SELF TEST**

| 1 | C | 16 | C | 31 | A |
|---|---|----|---|----|---|
| 2 | A | 17 | B | 32 | D |
| 3 | B | 18 | C | 33 | A |
| 4 | A | 19 | D | 34 | D |
| 5 | B | 20 | C | 35 | B |
| 6 | C | 21 | A | 36 | C |
| 7 | C | 22 | B | 37 | A |
| 8 | D | 23 | D | 38 | C |
| 9 | B | 24 | C | 39 | A |
| 10 | A | 25 | A | 40 | B |
| 11 | A | 26 | B | 41 | B |
| 12 | B | 27 | C | 42 | A |
| 13 | D | 28 | D | 43 | D |
| 14 | D | 29 | C | 44 | B |
| 15 | C | 30 | C | 45 | B |

**ESSAY QUESTIONS**

1. Hebb suggested that arousal was an important factor in motivation. People are the most efficient when they are at an optimal-level of arousal. Furthermore, he suggested that arousal is not the result of the stimulus but that it is the internal response to the stimulus that produces behavior, rather arousal is the energizes behavior, but does not direct it. This change in the view of arousals role in motivation began the transition to more cognitive views of motivation.

2. Maslow saw motivation as a hierarchy. At the bottom of the hierarchy are fundamental physiological needs. The motivation to meet these needs are drives to meet these biological needs such as hunger. As you fulfill needs on the bottom of the hierarchy you are able to move up to meet other needs and the final need of self-actualization. Self-actualization is a need in which people strive to realize their unique human potential. He believed that all people are naturally motivated to meet the need of self-actualization but that it cannot be achieved if the lower needs are not met first.

3. Ekman's research supports the idea that facial expressions are universal. They found that different cultures can easily interpret many facial expressions of other cultures. Also, people are very good at detecting changes in facial expressions. Support against the universality of facial expressions comes from the facts that facial expressions are not always accurate and that the accepted occasions of facial

expressions vary across cultures. For example, smiling at a funeral is accepted and encouraged in some cultures, but not in others.

4. Insulin and leptin are two important hormones in weight maintenance. Insulin allows glucose to be taken into body cells and is produced by the pancreas. Leptin in produced by the fat cells themselves. Both hormones send signals to the hypothalamus as part of the weight control process.

5. Tice and colleagues looked at impulse control from the perspective that break downs in impulse control are the result of a person's strategy to make themselves feel better. Her research showed that people who are not in a good mood are more likely to choose immediate rather than delayed gratification, eat unhealthy food and delay tedious tasks. This research supports the idea that we can control undesirable behaviors, but that when we are feeling bad, we often chose the quick fix over desirable behaviors.

## CHAPTER TWELVE

**SELF TEST**

| 1 | C | 16 | B | 31 | B |
|---|---|----|---|----|---|
| 2 | D | 17 | C | 32 | A |
| 3 | B | 18 | C | 33 | D |
| 4 | B | 19 | A | 34 | D |
| 5 | A | 20 | B | 35 | C |
| 6 | B | 21 | A | 36 | C |
| 7 | D | 22 | D | 37 | A |
| 8 | A | 23 | D | 38 | B |
| 9 | B | 24 | D | 39 | C |
| 10 | D | 25 | B | 40 | D |
| 11 | C | 26 | B | 41 | B |
| 12 | D | 27 | B | 42 | A |
| 13 | B | 28 | C | 43 | C |
| 14 | D | 29 | D | 44 | A |
| 15 | C | 30 | A | 45 | C |

**ESSAY QUESTIONS**

1.  The two main criticisms of Freud's theory is that it is sexist and cannot be empirically tested. Freud's theory is very derogatory in its depiction of women which raises criticisms. The theory also is hard to test scientifically because it has many poorly defined terms, it uses the unconscious to explain any behavior and because Freud failed to distinguish between his observations and his inferences. All of these things make it a theory that is hard to test. Another criticism is that the field of psychology itself has moved beyond Freud and other big personality theories, so good or bad, it is no longer needed.

2.  Skinner focuses on observable behaviors, not the unconscious to explain personality development. People's personalities are the result of what they have learned from their environment and is the sum of their learned tendencies. Since personality is the result of learning and reinforcement than personality can be changed. The behavioral approach also believes that evolution has played a role in personality development. People who learned to hunt cooperatively and had a personality conducive to community living survived and thus passed that trait on to future generations. (28-30)

3.  According to Rotter, people either have internal or external locus of control. Locus of control impacts your personality and how you view the world. One who has an internal locus of control, sees themselves as being in control of their lives and have a need to control their environment. One with an external locus of

control believes they have little control over their lives and are more likely to believe their successes and failures are due to something other than themselves.

4. Positive psychology focuses on well-being, contentment, hope, optimism and happiness. Their research indicates that people, even those with poor living conditions, are generally happy. Personality, adaptation and culture are all factors that impact happiness. Also, people who are involved and productive are happier.

5. Although the personality traits of people from different cultures can be measured with the same Five Factor Model, this does not mean that they have the same personalities. While researchers have found the Five Factors to exist across different cultures, the variance is substantial. Personality scores vary significantly across different cultures and the the largest amount of variance is found in the individual. Further, personality must be viewed in the cultural context and the culture must also consider its own definition of personality. What one culture defines as *extraversion* may be different in another culture even though both are considered descriptive relative to their own culture.

## CHAPTER THIRTEEN

**SELF TEST**

| 1 | A | 16 | B | 31 | A |
|---|---|----|---|----|---|
| 2 | C | 17 | D | 32 | C |
| 3 | D | 18 | B | 33 | D |
| 4 | B | 19 | D | 34 | C |
| 5 | C | 20 | C | 35 | A |
| 6 | C | 21 | C | 36 | C |
| 7 | C | 22 | B | 37 | A |
| 8 | D | 23 | A | 38 | B |
| 9 | B | 24 | A | 39 | C |
| 10 | C | 25 | A | 40 | A |
| 11 | B | 26 | D | 41 | B |
| 12 | C | 27 | A | 42 | A |
| 13 | C | 28 | D | 43 | D |
| 14 | D | 29 | B | 44 | C |
| 15 | B | 30 | D | 45 | C |

**ESSAY QUESTIONS**

1. The fundamental attribution error is that people tend to ignore or minimize the situational influences and assume that another person's behavior is the result of that person's internal disposition. This error is made mostly because people use mental shortcuts and judgments are normally made within a limited context. Also, people like to put themselves in a better light. This leads to the actor-observer effect where people are more likely to attribute something that happens to themselves as being caused by the situation and things that happen to others to be the result of internal causes.

2. Social conformity can be reached by putting people into groups. People conform to the believes and attitudes of their peers and family groups. Also just putting them into a group of others who hold a different believe can get someone to conform. Asch's research showed that some people will conform to the group opinion even if they know it is wrong if the entire rest of the group agrees with the incorrect opinion. If the information given is vague, people will also conform to the group. Making the behavior of nonconformity a public behavior also increases conformity.

3. The bystander effect is that the willingness of people to help someone else decreases with the number of other bystanders that are present. This is in part due to the fact that people are less likely to determine that the event is in fact an

emergency when others are apparently showing lack of concern over the event. Diffusion of responsibility also contributes to the bystander effect. Because other people are around who are also doing nothing the person feels they cannot be held responsible for not responding. Also, the presence of others makes it more likely that you think someone else has already responded, ie called 911.

4. Motivational theory explains prejudice as being the result of competition. Individuals learn to dislike their competitors and then generalize those feelings to people of the same race, religion or culture. Cognitive theories explain prejudice as being the result of ways of organizing the world. People are exposed to more stimuli than they can handle on an individual basis and so people use mental shortcuts to help them make decisions. These shortcuts include illusory correlation and social categorization. Both motivational theory and cognitive theory explain prejudice as a result of over generalization, but differ in the source of the problem.

5. Social loafing is a decrease in an individual's performance when they are working in a group. Social loafing occurs when the individual's performance cannot be evaluated separately from the groups performance. As a consequence, as the group size increases so does the effects of social loafing. One way to minimize social loafing is to make the task itself more attractive. The dynamics of the group also impact social loafing; a cohesive, small, group where members know each other well is less likely to experiences social loafing. The leader of the group can also decrease social loafing by calling the members by name and indicating that individual evaluations will be conducted.

## CHAPTER FOURTEEN

**SELF TEST**

| 1 | A | 16 | B | 31 | C |
|----|---|----|---|----|---|
| 2 | C | 17 | D | 32 | B |
| 3 | D | 18 | C | 33 | C |
| 4 | C | 19 | D | 34 | D |
| 5 | B | 20 | A | 35 | B |
| 6 | C | 21 | A | 36 | D |
| 7 | D | 22 | B | 37 | B |
| 8 | A | 23 | B | 38 | D |
| 9 | D | 24 | D | 39 | D |
| 10 | D | 25 | A | 40 | B |
| 11 | B | 26 | A | 41 | A |
| 12 | C | 27 | C | 42 | D |
| 13 | B | 28 | B | 43 | D |
| 14 | A | 29 | C | 44 | C |
| 15 | D | 30 | D | 45 | B |

**ESSAY QUESTIONS**

1. PTSD, post traumatic stress disorder, is a psychological disorder that may occur after a person has experienced sever stress as the result of some type of disaster. Symptoms include recollections that are intrusive and vivid and occasional lapses in normal consciousness. Anxiety, depression and exceptionally aggressive behavior are also symptoms. These symptoms often interfere with normal functioning. Victims of violence, war, and natural disasters are at risk of developing PTSD. Both women and men can develop PTSD.

2. Two active coping styles are emotion-focused coping and problem-focused coping. Emotion-focused coping focuses on managing the feelings of stress and finding ways to feel better. This lacks effectiveness for a situation that is not going to change on its own. Problem-focused coping focuses on solving or managing the problem that is causing stress. This coping style is more effective in most situations since is eliminates the problem causing the stress.

3. Health psychologists focus on health promotion. They do this through studying health related behaviors, such as eating habits and exercise. Also they educate people about prevention and wellness. Health psychologists are also involved in reducing risky behaviors and increasing compliance with orders from the doctor.

4. Having control over one's environment has been shown to positively impact a person's sense of well being and health. This impact includes when a person only

has feeling of control, or has the illusion of control. If a person feels that they are in control of their health, they are more likely to maintain better social relationships, have healthier immune systems and adopt healthier behaviors.

5. Lazarus suggests that stress is the result of the interaction between the event itself and the person's evaluation of the event. He refers this interaction as an active negotiation between the demands of the events and a person's beliefs. Other cognitive researchers refer to the active negotiation as cognitive appraisal. Therefore, how a person view the stressor, whether in a positive or negative light, determines on how stressful the situation is. How familiar a person is with the event and if they believe the have the resources to deal with the event will impact that person's cognitive appraisal of the situation.

## CHAPTER FIFTEEN

**SELF TEST**

| 1 | A | 16 | C | 31 | A |
|---|---|----|---|----|---|
| 2 | D | 17 | C | 32 | B |
| 3 | B | 18 | B | 33 | A |
| 4 | D | 19 | A | 34 | C |
| 5 | A | 20 | B | 35 | C |
| 6 | D | 21 | B | 36 | B |
| 7 | A | 22 | C | 37 | A |
| 8 | D | 23 | D | 38 | B |
| 9 | B | 24 | C | 39 | D |
| 10 | B | 25 | D | 40 | B |
| 11 | C | 26 | D | 41 | D |
| 12 | D | 27 | C | 42 | A |
| 13 | D | 28 | D | 43 | C |
| 14 | A | 29 | B | 44 | D |
| 15 | A | 30 | C | 45 | A |

**ESSAY QUESTIONS**

1. Maladjusted behaviors are behaviors that are not typical, socially unacceptable, distressing to the person who exhibits the behavior or to the person's friends and family, maladaptive and the result of cognitive distortions. Maladaptive behaviors can be changed and do not necessarily mean the entire person is maladaptive, just specific behaviors.

2. Phobia is a fear that is excessive and disproportionate to the situation and causes the person to avoid the situation. Phobia's unlike many fears are not adaptive. Phobias are normally treated using behavior therapy

3. The diathesis-stress model suggests that some people are more vulnerable than others and when these people encounter certain experiences the disorder, such as depression or schizophrenia develops. This view concludes that disorders develop from a combination of factors, some genetic some environmental. People with high vulnerability are more likely to develop a disorder from lower levels of stress than someone with lower vulnerability.

4. The psychoanalytic model views obsessive-compulsive disorders as stemming from difficulties during the anal stage of development. The learning model views obsessive-compulsive behavior as being reinforcing because it reduces uncertainty and risk. The biological perspective views obsessive-compulsive

disorder as a brain disorder that has behavioral symptoms. They have come to this conclusion, partially from the results of brain imaging studies.

5. The monoamine theory of depression is a biological theory of depression. This theory states that depression is the result of a lack of monoamines or inefficient receptors for monoamines in the brain. Monoamines are a class of neurotransmitters that includes dopamine, norepinephrine, epinephrine, and serotonin. If monoamines are released but are not accepted at the receptor sires of the next neuron, people are depressed. The monoamine is then take back up by the releasing cell. Anti-depressant drugs stop this reuptake process, leaving the neurotransmitter to bind to the receptor site. Although the fact that anti-depressants work is evidence in support of this theory, the fact that the drugs take several weeks to have an effect is one of the criticisms of this theory. Another criticism comes from the fact that all people do not respond to the drugs.

---

## CHAPTER SIXTEEN

**SELF TEST**

| 1 | C | 16 | D | 31 | D |
|----|----|----|----|----|----|
| 2 | B | 17 | D | 32 | C |
| 3 | B | 18 | A | 33 | D |
| 4 | D | 19 | C | 34 | D |
| 5 | C | 20 | B | 35 | B |
| 6 | C | 21 | A | 36 | A |
| 7 | C | 22 | D | 37 | A |
| 8 | A | 23 | C | 38 | B |
| 9 | C | 24 | D | 39 | B |
| 10 | D | 25 | D | 40 | D |
| 11 | A | 26 | B | 41 | A |
| 12 | D | 27 | D | 42 | A |
| 13 | B | 28 | C | 43 | B |
| 14 | C | 29 | B | 44 | B |
| 15 | C | 30 | C | 45 | D |

**ESSAY QUESTIONS**

1.  Insight therapy has two basic assumptions: that being aware of one's motivations helps a person change and become more adapted and maladjustment is caused by unresolved conflicts that the person is unaware of. Psychoanalysis and Client-centered therapy are both insight therapies. Where psychoanalysis focuses on the past, and diminishes free will, client-centered therapy focuses on the present and future and that people can determine their own destinies.

2.  Behavior therapy focuses on the behaviors of the client and how new behaviors can be learned not on unconscious processes or motivations. Behavior is changed through conditioning principles. Cognitive therapy focuses on changing behavior by changing the thought and perceptions of the client. It is based on the ideas that cognitive activity affects behavior, these activities can be monitored and changed.

3.  There are 4 main types of psychotropic drugs, antianxiety drugs, antidepressant drugs, antimania drugs and antipsychotropic drugs. Antiaxiety drugs reduce feelings of stress and lowers excitability. Antidepressant drugs alter the levels of neurotransmitters and generally elevate the person's mood. Antimania drugs relieve the manic symptoms associated with bipolar disorder. Antipsychotic drugs reduce hostility and aggression as well as delusions.

4.  Codependence is when a member of a family becomes enmeshed in the problems of another family member. The codependent person is often full of fear, anger,

---

shame and pain, but they feel they cannot express these feelings because they must take care of the person who is maladjusted. Often a codependent person believes that if they were perfect they could help the other person.

5. The placebo effect is an effect that occurs because a person expects change and is not the result of the treatment. The double-blind technique, where neither the participant nor the researcher knows what treatment or lack there of they are receiving is one way to eliminate the placebo effect. The double-blind technique reduces demand characteristics, bias in the experiment that can result from the way the participant perceives the situation or becomes aware of the purpose of the study and thus the participant behaves in a certain way.

## CHAPTER SEVENTEEN

### SELF TEST

| | | | | | |
|---|---|---|---|---|---|
| 1 | C | 16 | D | 31 | A |
| 2 | D | 17 | C | 32 | B |
| 3 | D | 18 | A | 33 | A |
| 4 | B | 19 | C | 34 | D |
| 5 | D | 20 | D | 35 | A |
| 6 | A | 21 | C | 36 | D |
| 7 | C | 22 | D | 37 | C |
| 8 | B | 23 | D | 38 | A |
| 9 | B | 24 | B | 39 | C |
| 10 | B | 25 | D | 40 | D |
| 11 | A | 26 | A | 41 | A |
| 12 | B | 27 | C | 42 | D |
| 13 | A | 28 | B | 43 | C |
| 14 | D | 29 | B | 44 | A |
| 15 | A | 30 | B | 45 | C |

### ESSAY QUESTIONS

1. The 4 broad areas of I/O psychology are human resources psychology, motivation of job performance, job satisfaction and leadership. Human resource psychology focuses on helping employers to hire, train and evaluate their employees. Motivation of job performance focuses on how rewards relate to successful performance and the relationship between management and employees. Job satisfaction of employees and managers are assessed and leadership looks at the define attributes of leaders.
2. Psychologist serves as researchers, policy or program evaluators, advocates and expert witnesses for the legal system. Researchers examine how juries decide cases, and how they assign blame or responsibility for a crime. Also, researchers look at why and who commits crimes. As policy or program evaluators, psychologists help determine if programs are actually working. Psychologists are also called upon to be advocates, to help shape policy on education. Finally, as expert witnesses, psychologists help determine whether someone is competent to stand trial and if they are insane.
3. There are three basic levels or prevention, primary, secondary, and tertiary. Primary prevention involves aims at reducing the incident of new cases of a disorder. This level of prevention typically targets groups of people rather than individuals. The secondary level of prevention involves the diagnosis of new

mental health problems in their early stages. This type of prevention often occurs at crisis prevention centers. The tertiary level of intervention deals with those individuals that have full-blown psychological disorders and tries to eliminate or reduce the problem.

4. Sports psychologists help athletes by improving sports performance. They do this by teaching athletes mental strategies that helps them be more effective and over come obstacles. Second, sport psychologists try to enhance the sports experience for young participants. Finally, they help with injury rehabilitation.

5. Time allocation, classroom rules and pacing are all important in efficient classroom management. Proper time allocation includes starting lessons on time, minimizing time spent on routine procedures and minimizing time spent on discipline. All of these things increase the amount of time students spend on-task, actively engaged in learning. Classroom rules need to be clearly set, procedures need to be established, and the expectations of the teacher need to be established at the beginning of the school year to maximize classroom efficiency. Finally , the pacing of the class, and the teachers voice needs to be varied to help students stay on task and maximize learning.